MW00614082

NEXT LIFE

a novel

DAVE SWAVELY

The painting shown on the cover is a 1737 oil sketch by Giambattista Tiepolo for his larger painting, St. Dominic in Glory. *Dominic died at 51, the same age at which Tim Carler was taken up into heaven.*

 Cruciform Fiction

"As a Tolkien scholar and theological educator, I found *Next Life* to be **an interesting and refreshing melding of the fantastic and the profound**. Not only does the book challenge current perceptions of the afterlife, but it encourages the reader to go back and explore what Scripture says about our eternal existence. More than that, and even differently than classic texts like *The Great Divorce*, it **had me longing for eternity with my Lord**."

Ike Reeder, President, Birmingham Theological Seminary

"Dave Swavely's novella, *Next Life*, is a unique take on one man's trip to heaven. More thought-provoking than awe-inspiring, in keeping with the personality of the author's protagonist, it causes the reader to focus on aspects of heaven they'd perhaps not considered before, rather than the external attributes that are so typical of "heaven tourism" books. Still, the protag's **visions of Nazi Germany and Victorian London—or are they reality?—add another dimension to an already intriguing story**."

Sharon K. Souza, award-winning author of *What We Don't Know*

Next Life: A Novel

Print / PDF ISBN: 978-1-941114-30-8
Mobipocket ISBN: 978-1-941114-31-5
ePub ISBN: 978-1-941114-32-2

Published by Cruciform Press, Minneapolis, Minnesota. Copyright © 2018 by Dave Swavely

Apart from dialogue passages, Scripture quotations are from the ESV Bible (The Holy Bible, English Standard © 2001 by Crossway).

Table of Contents

Chapter 1

A True Trip to Heaven

I lay awake in my bed for months wishing I would die, and one night I actually did.

At least that's what I think happened. Whether you believe that, or anything else I tell you in this book, is up to you. But remember that "truth is stranger than fiction" sometimes, or if you prefer to think of this as a made-up story, "truth is no stranger to fiction." Either way I hope you'll be able to get a sideways view of the truth, as C. S. Lewis called it, by hearing what I have to tell you.

I didn't dream all this—that I can assure you. Maybe it was more of a "vision," like those experienced by Isaiah, Ezekiel, and the apostle Paul. Although Paul, for his part, didn't just say he *saw* heaven. He said he was "caught up" into it and seemed to have spent a while there, like I did. However, he did add (twice), "Whether in the body or out of the body I do not know, God knows" (2 Cor. 12:2-3), so there was definitely some ambiguity and mystery in his mind about what had actually happened. My experience was similar to his in that way, too.

Though I was known for many years as "Pastor

Tim Carler," I've never claimed to be a prophet or an apostle. In fact, I'm not even a pastor anymore. I committed some inexcusable sins, was suspected of worse and subjected to the rumor mill, and ended up in disgrace and despair—which explains the months of sleepless nights. I'll tell you more about that later, but for now let me add that I'm also not a "charismaniac" who believes that all the miracles in the Bible are still happening to the same degree today. I even wrote a book once explaining why I think they don't. And the experience I'm writing about here hasn't changed my basic beliefs about any issue in Scripture (in fact it has strengthened quite a few of them).

I've combed the Bible and read several lengthy books about heaven by respected authors, and I don't believe anything I tell you will contradict any clear teaching of the Word, or even most of the opinions expressed in those books. For example, Randy Alcorn's 500-page treatise called *Heaven* is surprisingly consistent with many things I'm going to tell you, which is impressive considering the fact that he hasn't been there yet. I recommend that book to you if you want to know more about your next life, because in the one you're reading I'll be focusing on some amazing adventures that were unique to me.

If you do read Alcorn, however, keep in mind that his understanding is over-literal at times, especially when he takes the visions in Revelation as actual descriptions of places and events. Those passages are more like movies that *represent* reality in a symbolic way, but are not identical to it. Along those lines, he makes a great point over and over again in the book that there is more continuity between this life and the next than most people think, and that we *can* comprehend many things about it because God has revealed them in his Word. But he emphasizes the continuity and comprehension so much that the reader can miss the fact that in many ways heaven is still infinitely beyond our understanding, and even our imagination. No doubt God wants it to be that way while we remain in this world.

So I won't be giving detailed descriptions of the places I visited, and I also won't be crafting my narrative very carefully. I was a pastor for over twenty years, so this book may sound more like a sermon than a story sometimes—I'm just "writing what I know." I'm basically going to tell you some of what happened in the order I remember it, and comment on it along the way. I can't tell you all of it, for several reasons, but what I can I want to write down quickly before something else happens that might prevent me from doing so.

Before I do that, however, I want to address a few questions that might be in your mind and answer them as best I can so that there won't be any unnecessary barriers to your enjoyment and edification.

First, why me? Why was I chosen to have such an exceptional experience? I've thought a lot about this. It's certainly not because I'm an exceptional person. As a disgraced pastor who hurt a lot of people by my sins, I deserve the opposite of special privileges from God. But maybe that has something to do with why he chose me, because of many similar stories in Scripture.

Jacob saw a heavenly ladder, had a physical encounter with the pre-incarnate Jesus Christ, and became a namesake for all God's people, but he was a deceiver, thief, polygamist, etc. In fact, I don't think the Bible ever records any good deeds that Jacob did, except at the end of his life when he blessed his descendants. Samson and David and Solomon and the aforementioned Paul did all kinds of great things for God, but they were idolaters and adulterers and murderers. And so on.

I used to think I was special because of my achievements, and that the more I accomplished the more special I would become. But now I wonder if I'm actually more eligible to be used by God because I blew it and nobody would think any privilege I receive is because of me. God chooses people who are obviously undeserving so they can become illustrations of his grace, to show that He's the only one who is truly special.

Also, God may have had a sense of humor in picking me, because I always used to say, "I'll never be a best-selling author—I don't have a big church and I haven't been to heaven and back." Providence seems to have assured that I will never pastor a big church, but perhaps it will give with the one hand what it has taken away with the other.

Or maybe I was chosen because I'm a big loser *and* a decent writer, so I could record this amazing account but not take any credit for it.

Hopefully all this talk about my failures will mitigate any concern about me being arrogant because of my metaphysical experiences, or narcissistic in writing about them. I feel similar to Paul when he wrote about his trip to heaven in 2 Corinthians 12:7, "to keep me from becoming conceited because of the surpassing greatness of the revelations, a thorn was given me in the flesh, a messenger of Satan to harass me, to keep me from becoming conceited." I've also had a terrible infirmity that is related to my reputation—as Paul's probably was, judging from the context in 2 Corinthians.

Another similarity to Paul is that I won't be sharing a lot of the things that I learned on my trip (he "heard inexpressible words, which a man is not permitted to speak"). God hasn't allowed me to remember and record anything that would constitute new revelation about himself or his mysterious plans. Everything I share with you will either reiterate or illustrate truth that has already been revealed in the Bible. It will all be consistent with what God has already said, unlike the rest of the supposedly "non-fiction" books that have been published about visits to heaven.

"Speaking of those terrible heaven tourism books," you might say, "going to heaven itself is not controversial—that happens all the time when believers die. But coming back afterward is harder to swallow." Well, that's another way I'm like Paul (notwithstanding our many differences). When he said, "whether in the body or out of the body I do not know, God knows," he meant that he didn't know whether he had actually died or not, and I'm not sure either.

It wasn't a dream like in *Pilgrim's Progress*, but it could have been a series of visions, or if you prefer you could conclude that I was hallucinating because of all the devastating emotional and spiritual stress I was under. But it's hard to imagine that an already impaired mind could conjure such vivid, detailed, and extensive scenes from the lives of numerous persons unknown to me—not to mention the ones with famous people like the Jewish Patriarchs, Adolph Hitler, and the two Charleses (Spurgeon and Dickens).

One more matter before I revisit those places and times with you: I want to dedicate this book to my family. Usually dedications are brief blurbs on a page before the first chapter, but what I have to say won't fit there.

First, to my children: Early on after my repentance I prayed repeatedly that God would spare you from suffering any consequences for my sin, and place them all on me. Looking back now at all that has occurred, I believe that for the most part he granted my wish, which explains why I have suffered so much and why you have been so blessed. I pray now that this book will be a source of even more blessings for you.

Last, but certainly not least (especially in light of what you're about to read), I dedicate this book to my wife Lynn. Only a person deluded by the most irrational prejudice, or perhaps clouded somehow by her husband's faults, would not recognize that she is one of the most special and spiritually influential angels God ever placed on this planet. From the dozens of hurting people she has housed and loved in our home, to the hundreds of students she has blessed by starting and running two unique Christian schools, and the many others she has touched as a friend and pastor's wife through the years, Lynn's impact on this world for the kingdom of Christ is incalculable. This book is a public tribute to her, and a personal thank you for her allowing me to be a part of her extraordinary life so far, and the exciting adventures yet to come.

For my family and for all of you, I hope the time you spend reading this book will have an effect on you in line with this famous quote by C. S. Lewis from *Mere Christianity*, part of which Lynn recently wrote on the "chalk wall" in our kitchen…

> Hope is one of the Theological virtues. This means that a continual looking forward to the eternal world is not (as some modern people think) a form of escapism or wishful thinking, but one of the things a Christian is meant to do. It does not mean that we are to leave the present world as it is. If you read history you will find that the Christians who did most for the present world were just those who thought most of the next. The Apostles themselves, who set on foot the conversion of the Roman Empire, the great men who built up the Middle Ages, the English Evangelicals who abolished the Slave Trade, all left their mark on Earth, precisely because their minds were occupied with Heaven. It is since Christians have largely ceased to think of the other world that they have become so ineffective in this. Aim at Heaven and you will get earth "thrown in": aim at earth and you will get neither.

Chapter 2

Beggar at the Feast

They say that when you get to heaven you'll be surprised by three things: who's there, who's not there, and most of all, that you're there. There's a lot of truth to that, but with a caveat on the "surprised" part. It's true that all those things would be surprising to us while we're in this world, because the realities of heaven don't fit readily with our natural, earthly perspectives. But once we're there, we won't actually be surprised, because one of the features of heaven is that we will share God's perspective, and he's never surprised by anything.

Much of what I experienced when my soul left my body on that fateful night will indeed be surprising to you who are reading this, as it would have been to me if someone had told me these things. So in this chapter I'll share the initial events (what I can remember anyway) with the thread of those surprises running through my account.

Let me start with the last surprise mentioned in saying above, which is one of the biggest…that *I was there*.

The possibility that I could die in my bed was not too far-fetched during those excruciating months of suffering. At times, including that night, my body was so wracked with pain and pressure that I often thought I might have a heart attack or stroke (which actually may have been the case, though I never saw a doctor or made any other attempt to solve the mystery). And with how bad I felt, that wouldn't have been entirely unwelcome, as long as it ended up with me out of this world and didn't leave me here in even worse suffering.

But it was definitely a surprise to find myself, in the middle of one of my fits of desperation, suddenly transported to an entirely different realm of existence.

The supposedly "non-fiction" heaven tourism books that have been all the rage in recent years lose credibility with me from the beginning, and that's not because they've been written by people with suspicious names like Burpo and Malarkey. (As if that fact wasn't already stranger than fiction, the little boy named Malarkey who supposedly visited heaven admitted later that his story was, well, a bunch of Malarkey. I'm not sure we needed that admission—it wasn't as if God hadn't already given us a clue.)

I'm skeptical of most, if not all, of those other stories because they start with the person drifting out of their body, seeing and hearing things in the hospital room or wherever in the same way they saw and heard things while they were alive. And then they keep on seeing and hearing everything that way while they're in heaven.

The problem is, disembodied souls don't have eyes or ears!

When we die, our bodies stay on the earth, and are buried or cremated eventually. Our souls are the only parts of us that proceed to the next life, and they don't have any physical senses because they are not physical, but spiritual. Therefore, since the whole "floating out of your body" phenomenon is a function of earthly physics, it can only happen when you're still alive in this world—not when you're passing into heaven. And we know that those same kinds of things can happen entirely in your brain, of course, because people often experience them in dreams. But the transition into the next world is not a physical process, and it's certainly not a trip through a tunnel with a light at the end—it's more like slipping sideways into an utterly new dimension. If we perceive people or things on earth after we pass (more on that later too), it will be in an entirely different way than we did before.

So I'd be more inclined to believe those stories of people visiting heaven if they described their perception of this world as being shockingly different from the way they viewed it when they were living—and also if they didn't go on to say things that were clearly contradictory to the Scriptures. But let's get back to my story…

My soul *was* immediately without a body, and I *did* perceive everything in a very different way. In fact, my perception was so transformed that I will have difficulty communicating with you about it here. I'll do my best, but I will have to use words that are too limited to fully capture the realities, and will even have to make up some terms in an attempt to discuss them. The communication that takes place between God, angels, and human souls is not in English, of course, and spiritual beings in heaven don't have lungs, mouths, or lips (with a few exceptions that I'll tell you about). So I'll record what I remember of what was "said," but I won't use quotation marks like in a normal account, because the communication was so different than our experience on earth, and because I can't put the exact meaning into English words anyway. I'll use words like "said" and "told," but only as an accommodation to our lesser, cruder language.

I'll also refer to myself and other humans in heaven as "souls," and the other beings (the ones we call angels) as "spirits." This is not a technical or biblical distinction, but one that will help you to understand my narrative, and to remember that bodilessness is the normal state of humans in heaven, prior to the return of Christ and the resurrection of our bodies.

The "Intermediate State" after death and before the final resurrection is described in 2 Corinthians 5:1-4. There Paul says, "We know that if the tent that is our earthly home [our body] is destroyed, we have a building from God, a house not made with hands, eternal in the heavens. For in this tent we groan, longing to put on our heavenly dwelling, if indeed by putting it on we may not be found naked. For while we are still in this tent, we groan, being burdened—not that we would be unclothed, but that we would be further clothed, so that what is mortal may be swallowed up by life."

What he's saying is that if we die before Christ returns, we will be temporarily "found naked" or "unclothed" in the sense of being souls without bodies during the Intermediate State. This is not an ideal situation for us, because we were created to be souls *with* bodies, so Paul adds that it would be preferable if we could be "further clothed, so that what is mortal may be swallowed up by life." He is referring to the hope that Christ might return *before we die*, because in Greek "further clothed" can be translated "clothed on over"—there are multiple prepositional prefixes added to the verb. The hope that the "mortal may be swallowed up by life" also conveys the same idea.

The threat of being separated from our bodies is one of the reasons why death is always a negative thing in Scripture. But even though dying is far less ideal than being "changed, in a moment, in the twinkling of an eye" when Christ returns (1 Cor. 15:51-52, a parallel passage), it is still preferable to remaining here on this cursed earth. Paul goes on to say in 2 Corinthians 5:6-8, "So we are always of good courage. We know that while we are at home in the body we are away from the Lord, for we walk by faith, not by sight. Yes, we are of good courage, and we would rather be away from the body and at home with the Lord."

That's what I "shifted" into on that sleepless night—the Intermediate State where my soul was strangely without my body, but was also gloriously in the presence of the Lord. I will call that realm the IS from now on, because I'll be referring to it a lot, and for another interesting reason I'll get to a little later. But for now I want to talk about, as best I can, what it was like to be in the presence of the Lord.

That was the most profound and amazing thing about my whole experience. I can't really put it into words, and that's much more than a cliché in this case. But I'll make an effort anyway.

I didn't actually meet the risen Jesus Christ "in the

flesh" until a little while after I arrived, because I had to be given a temporary body or "sheath" in order to do that (more on that later). But as soon as I left my body, just as the passage says, my soul was immediately living in the unmitigated presence of the triune God—the Father, Son, and Holy Spirit. How Jesus could be bodily present in one place, but also spiritually present everywhere, is still a mystery to me. But it was obviously and unquestionably true. All three members of the Trinity were with me at all times, or rather I should say I was with them, because there was an overwhelming sense of God being everywhere. I had never felt anything even remotely like it before—not even in the times during my life that I thought I was experiencing the presence of God. Those times thinly echoed the reality of the next life, but were so different as to be almost incomparable.

God is always everywhere, but we don't recognize or experience it fully, or even close, because of the sinfulness in ourselves and the brokenness in our fallen world.

But in the IS….Wow! *Indescribable*, like I said, but I'll keep pressing on anyway…

So many things became much more clear than they'd ever been to me. The clarity hit me like a lightning bolt, in fact. First was my sinfulness and how undeserving I was of anything good from God. The best way I can describe it is to refer to the experiences of Isaiah and Peter in the Scriptures. When Isaiah's vision took him into the presence of God, he said, "Woe is me! For I am lost; for I am a man of unclean lips, and I dwell in the midst of a people of unclean lips;

for my eyes have seen the King, the Lord of hosts!" (Isa. 6:5). And when Jesus calmed the storm and Peter realized that God himself was in the boat, "he fell down at Jesus' knees, saying, 'Depart from me, for I am a sinful man, O Lord'" (Luke 5:8). Multiply those earthly reactions by a thousand and you might have a sense of what it was like for a man like me, whose life had been so filled with sin, to find himself in the presence of a holy and wrathful God. But it was only times a thousand, rather than a million, since I was a new person now, and because of what also happened at the same time...

Before any pangs of horror and despair could gain any significant foothold in my heart, and even before I could express them like Isaiah and Peter did, another awareness simultaneously overwhelmed me—one of forgiveness, love, and purpose.

After Isaiah confessed his sinfulness, God sent an angel to touch his lips with a coal from the altar, saying, "Behold, this has touched your lips; your guilt is taken away, and your sin atoned for" (Isa. 6:7). Then Isaiah was commissioned as a prophet, to speak God's Word to his people (vv. 8-10). And when Peter recognized his unworthiness in the fishing boat, Jesus told him, "Do not be afraid; from now on you will be catching men." (Luke 5:10).

Multiply the relief and joy that those men felt by a million, or rather a million millions, and you might have a sense of what it was like for me. "Grace greater than all our sin" and "where sin abounds, grace abounds even more" took on new meaning, to say the least. I knew beyond a shadow of doubt that I was forgiven totally and loved infinitely, and the unreserved acceptance of this awesome Sovereign/Father, Savior/ Brother, and Sealer/Comforter so far superseded any guilt and condemnation as to render the latter truly inconsequential. And like Isaiah and Peter, he actually had some exciting work for me to do in his service.

But speaking of the presence of God in relation to my sins, remembering it now makes me think of a comment a friend of mine made once about Psalm 103:12, which says, "As far as the east is from the west, so far does he remove our transgressions from us." My friend said that if you go north or south, you'll eventually end up going the opposite direction again, so north and south are not infinitely apart from one another. But if you go east, you'll never be going west, or vice versa. That's how far God has put our sins away from us— infinitely far—and that's about all I have to say about my own sins, in case you've been wondering about the ones that caused me such disgrace and despair. They're gone, and gone forever, and now I'm moving forward to serve the Lord who redeemed me.

My experience also reminds me of the short story by Josh Harris called "The Room," where he imagines finding a filing system full of cards containing all the sins he's committed, but then Jesus appears and blots them all out with his blood, and sends him out forgiven, with the privilege of writing new cards. The feelings the narrator experiences in that story are something like mine on that night...times a million millions.

Chapter 3

Not Many Noble

Finding out that I was in heaven wasn't the only surprising thing about the place, however. Another was *who else was there*, as the old saying goes. I wasn't actually surprised myself by this once I was there, because my perspective was totally changed from when I was on the earth. But from an earthly, human point of view, most people would actually be shocked at the kind of people I met there. And it wasn't just that "there were not many wise according to the flesh, not many mighty, not many noble," like it says in 1 Corinthians 1:26. It also gave new meaning to Jesus' saying that "I did not come to call the righteous, but sinners" (Mark 2:17).

I had the clear sense that people with impeccable reputations on earth were in the minority among the citizens of heaven. The next life is filled with people who had bad character for much or all of their lives, or who failed miserably at some point in pathetic and even scandalous ways. It seems that for the most part, only people whose lives were deeply broken in some way are able to really grasp the gospel and fully trust in Christ, which echoes the first part of the verse mentioned above: "It is not those who are healthy who need a physician, but those who are sick."

The most powerful illustrations of this—and that's an understatement—were the two "tour guides" I was given on my trip. And that's probably why God chose them for me, so I and you would be "hit over the head" with the fact that heaven is a place for the undeserving, and that because of God's infinite grace, anyone can end up there.

Jeff and Steve had been serial killers during their lives on earth.

Yes, you heard me right, and I wouldn't joke about something like that—though I do have joy when I think about them, because of what wonderful people they have now become by God's redeeming grace, and how the relative footnote of their past lives stands as a profound illustration of the freeness of that grace. The terrible sins and crimes they had committed have now been washed away like tears in a flood. Those horrors are not even thought about very often in the next life, and when they are it is only for the purpose of high-lighting the mercy of the Lord. (He controls everything we are able to know and think about, in a way that is always for our good.)

I call them Jeff and Steve (names are not the same in the IS, where most communication is by thought and not in English) because I think they were Jeffrey Dahmer and Stephen Morin. I say "think they were" because in the limited amount of information I was able to glean from them, their stories matched up with those notorious murderers. I didn't meet anyone who knew them and could confirm their identity, and perhaps God limited my knowledge so that what I say would not be a concrete revelation of anyone's presence in heaven.

I think that may be why I didn't meet anyone I already knew while I was there, by the way—including my father, who had professed faith in Christ just before he died. I'll have to wait until a later time to find out for sure about him and other people I've known, but I can tell you that there were many, many people in heaven who were saved in the last moments of their lives. Someone had prayed for them or shared the gospel with them at some point during their lives, and God graciously gave them faith as they passed out of it, so they also could forever serve as illustrations of his sovereign mercy.

Speaking of people sharing the gospel, one reason I think that my two new friends were Jeffrey Dahmer and Stephen Morin was because of the conversion stories they shared with me. I checked later and found that it was consistent with the news accounts about the two murderers. For example, Jeff said that not long after he had repented and believed while in jail, he was killed by another inmate because he was telling too many people about Jesus. Then his killer tried to exonerate himself by claiming that Jeff was a hypocrite who hadn't really changed. I suppose that could have happened to some other criminal in prison for multiple murders, but it sure sounds like Jeffrey Dahmer to me.

Steve told me that the police were closing in on him one day, and that he had determined to end his life in a gun battle with them. But on that same day, before they caught up with him, he visited a church building and sat in a pew half-praying and wondering if there was any hope for someone like him. Thinking there probably wasn't, he went back to his plan for a final murder/suicide and abducted one more woman from a supermarket parking lot. But this woman turned out to be a Christian who prayed for him and told him about Jesus, and he ended up letting her go and surrendering to the police peacefully as God's Spirit began working in him. He fully committed to Christ while in prison, and willingly submitted to the death penalty as a fruit of his repentance. That all fits very well with the reported story of Stephen Morin.

So I'll call them Jeff and Steve, because even if they were not those famous criminals, their presence in heaven still shows that people like Dahmer and Morin will be there.

Do you have a problem with that? I know I would have before this all happened to me—and I don't just mean my trip to heaven, but also my own sin and disgrace. If you have a problem with the idea of serial killers being in heaven, maybe you don't really understand the gospel of grace, or how deeply offensive your own sins are to a holy God. Maybe you have some things backward, like an article I read by an atheist who accused Christianity of being fundamentally flawed because repentant murderers like Dahmer and Morin might be in heaven while at least some of their innocent victims are not. Rather than invalidating the gospel message, however, that possibility actually demonstrates the essence of it. The truth of justification by faith alone means that in heaven it will be very clear "that no one can boast" (Eph. 2:8-9), a fact which couldn't have been more obvious to me while I was there.

What about *who was not there*? The old saying suggests that we'll be surprised by that as well, and I can confirm that part too. As I already implied, there are far fewer "religious" people in heaven than we would ever imagine. We tend to think of the citizenry being primarily "good people," with the occasional bad seed like the thief on the cross thrown in for good measure. But there is no one in heaven who was truly good in God's eyes during their life on earth (or even "innocent," as the atheist writer described the serial killers' victims). Every one of us is a sinner by birth and by choice, having proceeded from Adam and inherited both his condemnation and his sinful nature.

This is something else that becomes so clear in the presence of God: our entire race was spiritually separated from him when we fell into sin in the Garden of Eden, just like the angels who fell from heaven when Lucifer led a rebellion against the Creator. And just as there was never any way that the fallen angels could be restored to fellowship with God, so we as fallen humans became equally opposed to him in our nature and undeserving of anything good. Our only hope, therefore, lies in the redemption of Jesus Christ, the eternal Son of God who became a human being to remove the barrier of sin between God and us by his sacrifice on the cross, and in the transformation of our hearts by the Holy Spirit.

Remember Jesus himself said "I did not come to call the righteous, but sinners to repentance." He is "our great God and Savior Jesus Christ, who gave himself for us to redeem us from all lawlessness and to purify for himself a people for his own possession who are zealous for good works" (Titus 2:13). The last part of that verse shows that people do change for good as a result of being redeemed by Christ, but they don't get redeemed *because* they made a change for good. And in many cases, like the thief on the cross, they don't repent until the very end of their lives, and that change might not be seen by many others—or even any others. Remember that we only know about the conversion of the thief on the cross because Luke recorded the episode in his gospel. If he hadn't, only Jesus (and maybe a few onlookers) would have known about it.

Though I didn't meet a large number of other souls on my trip, I can tell you with confidence from what I did experience (and from the Scriptures) that there is no one in heaven who did anything to deserve being there. And there are a staggering number of souls who were never known by others to be believers. Many of them were saved while passing out of this life, but others just never looked much like Christians during their lives. But they were disciplined by God, sometimes to the point of death itself (1 Cor. 11:30-32), and they were broken enough by their sin to know that Christ was their only hope, like the tax collector who had nothing to offer but simply prayed, "God, be merciful to me the sinner."

"I tell you," Jesus said, "this man went to his house justified rather than the other." "The other" was not just a very religious and moral person, but a Pharisee who was a leader in the church (Luke 18:9-14). There are not any people like that man in heaven, because such people trust in *who they are* ("I thank God that I am not as bad as this tax collector") and *what they do* ("I fast and give money to the church") to make them right with God, instead of trusting in Jesus and what he has done for us.

I was surprised to find out that I was in heaven, and many religious people will be shocked to find out they're not (Matt. 7:21-23). Don't get me wrong—if you are a true Christian, the loved ones that you've had spiritual fellowship with in this life will be there, as 1 Thessalonians 4:13-18 promises. But you will be surprised by the absence of many who you knew as mere acquaintances, or as public figures, who seemed like good people from an outward perspective.

Chapter 4

Surprised by Joy (and Pain)

There were many other surprises about heaven that are not covered in that old saying about who's there and who's not. I'll mention a few more here, and one of them is *how much light and darkness* there is in heaven.

When I say light, I am using the term in two ways the Bible often does, to refer to God's unique glory and perfect righteousness. First, I couldn't have possibly anticipated, nor can I fully express here, how central the glory of God is to the heavenly realm. That's another problem with most, if not all, of the popular "heaven tourism" books—they focus almost exclusively on the pleasures of human beings, rather than the glory of God, which is what heaven is really all about. I don't want you to get the wrong impression by the fact that I started by talking about my own joy at being there. That was just because I was discussing the famous saying about surprises in heaven. But by far the strongest impression made upon me during my visit, and anyone else who makes it to heaven, is that of the indescribable glory of God. A sense of his utter worthiness and majesty dominates all the thoughts and feelings of his creatures, and every experience is defined and understood by it.

For example, one of the reasons there is no sin in heaven is because of the dominant, all-pervasive sense of God's presence and glory. Sin in this fallen world often occurs when we don't believe or remember that God is right there with us. If Jesus was bodily present, standing right next to us, we wouldn't do most of the bad things we do, or even think about them. In reality, he *is* present with us at all times, but we don't realize it. In heaven that never happens, and that combined with our sinful impulses being removed makes it almost impossible for anyone to sin. (I say "almost" because Satan, his demons, and Adam and Eve all sinned in the direct presence of God, so to permanently confirm us in righteousness we will need to be in eternal union with Christ—a privilege they did not have, but fortunately we do.)

To understand more what I mean by the surprising amount of light in heaven, imagine the times in your life when you were most in love. The ones you loved were "always with you" in the sense that you couldn't stop thinking about them, and you wanted nothing more than to please them because they were so amazingly beautiful and desirable to you. Multiply that times a million millions and you get an idea of what it's like to live in the light of God's presence.

But there was also much more *darkness* in heaven, and especially in the IS, than I could have possibly foreseen. By darkness I mean, first of all, the amount of knowledge of evil that I had there. We commonly think of heaven as a place where there won't be any awareness of bad things from the past, let alone those that are happening right now on the earth. But Revelation 6:10 clearly disproves that idea. It says that the souls of the martyrs "cried out with a loud voice, 'O Sovereign Lord, holy and true, how long before you will judge and avenge our blood on those who dwell on the earth?'" That passage, along with a number of others, makes it clear that people in heaven can be aware of both past and present evil, and even interact with it during the next life. That certainly was my experience, to an extent that would be shocking to most people, and probably will be as I continue to recount my adventures here.

Perhaps you've already been uncomfortably surprised by the dark evil in the past of my two "tour guides," Jeff and Steve, which both they and I were fully aware of (yet without it being debilitating or even depressing to any of us). If so, you'll be glad to know that particular example of "darkness" is probably the most difficult one to accept—that's why I wanted to put it out there early on in my narrative. But prepare yourself, because there will be more.

I also use the word "darkness" to refer to my relative ignorance—relative to what I thought would be the case. There was so much I didn't know or understand, so many mysteries not solved, and so few answers to questions I still have. God in his sovereignty was obviously keeping a tight rein on what I observed and comprehended; I guess he does the same during our earthly experience as well, but that's another thing we don't realize as much while we're here. I suppose he does this, both here and there, for our good, because he knows we can't handle knowing too much, and other people can't handle hearing too much from us. Also I came to suspect strongly that knowledge in the IS is much more limited than it will be in the ES (that's my nickname for the "Eternal State" that we will enter when Jesus returns, gives us our permanent glorified bodies, and creates the new heavens and earth). And that leads me to the last kind of "darkness" I experienced in the current heaven…

Believe it or not, much of the time I was there I was bothered by a nagging sense of incompleteness, not entirely unlike some of the feelings of depression I had in this life, though definitely not as bad. This discomfort came from the fact that I was "naked," to use Paul's words, and "longing to be clothed" with the new body I would receive at the resurrection. You might be as surprised by this as anything else I've said, because you're thinking that heaven is perfect, with no tears or pain, etc. But keep in mind those words were spoken about the new heavens and new earth (Rev. 21:1-4), not the Intermediate State. As long as there is a proliferation of sin in this universe, there will always be sadness and even tears, when someone has physical eyes to shed them. Jesus was a perfect human being, yet he was sad and cried (Luke 19:41-44, John 11:35), and Romans 8:22 says "the *whole creation* has been groaning together in the pains of childbirth until now." Certainly that includes the "heavens" as well as the earth, because God created both, and the next verse says that the groaning will not cease until Jesus returns and makes everything new.

Another surprise about heaven is that there are *both spiritual and physical aspects* to it. I already mentioned that many people (especially the heaven tourism authors) don't seem to realize that in the IS we normally exist as souls without bodies. But others may not realize that we sometimes do have temporary bodies, which God gives to us for various specific purposes.

This wouldn't be a surprise to Randy Alcorn, because in his book he actually suggests that we will have temporary bodies *the entire time* we're in the IS, up until the final resurrection when we get our new, permanent ones. To support that rather odd idea he has to explain away 2 Corinthians 5, the passage that says we will be "naked" and "unclothed" in the IS. Most of his errors about heaven, like that one, are a result of his over-literal interpretation, like when he seems to entirely miss the fact that "the New Jerusalem" is referring to the souls of people rather than buildings.

But Alcorn is right that there *are* physical aspects to the current heaven, including one of the best parts of it. Jesus himself, who is fully human as well as divine, still has a physical body. So there must be a physical place for him to dwell—though it's not like any place we've ever been, and I won't even attempt to describe it here. We don't have to be in a physical body to visit Christ in his, or to worship and fellowship with him— we will live fully and happily in his presence even when he is not present bodily. But sometimes while we are in the IS, God graciously allows us to take on a temporary body and meet with Christ "in the flesh." I did this, and it was one of the biggest thrills of my entire trip, partially because it gave me an exciting glimpse of our future existence in the ES, when we will be complete with our new bodies. But mostly it was exciting because I was able to be with my Lord and Savior in his full humanity, seeing him as he lived and died on the earth, right down to the nail prints in his hands.

I not only enjoyed worshiping Jesus in both soul and body, the way it was meant to be, but I was also able to talk to him face to face. Since I was in his presence and in communication with him (along with the Father and Spirit) all throughout my time in the IS, I didn't need this bodily meeting to be happy. But it was an extra special treat, to put it mildly. What I said to him and what he said to me in those moments is another thing I won't be describing here—it was just between me and him. But to summarize and help you understand the spiritual and physical aspects of heaven, think of it this way…

The Holy Trinity consists of two divine beings that are entirely spiritual, right? The Father and the Holy Spirit do not have physical bodies. But there is a member of the Godhead who does have one—the eternal Son, who was incarnated into the physical world, has sanctified it by becoming a part of it, and will restore it forever in the new heavens and earth. So because the Trinity itself is more or less "two-thirds spiritual and one-third physical" (pardon the oversimplification), it makes sense that the place "where God dwells" would be similar in its nature—a primarily spiritual realm with some physical aspects.

There are many surprises that I won't be talking about in this book (perhaps another time, if God allows), but here are just two more that relate to the adventures I will be sharing with you…

Another purpose for the temporary bodies that I nicknamed "sheaths" (to remind us that they're not our permanent ones) is so we can *visit the earth*. And not only that, but we can also *travel through time!*

That's another reason I call the Intermediate State the IS: you can pronounce it like the verb "is," which highlights the fact that we are not bound by time when we are there. God exists outside of time and sees all of it at once, and the same is true of space. So part of the wonder of God's unmediated presence is that we will no longer be limited to one particular "when" or "where." And the tasks the Lord had for me to do, when I was commissioned for service like Isaiah and Peter, were all in other times and places.

Chapter 5

Wrinkles in Time

Time will still exist in heaven—and that's not just true of the ES, but also the IS. The prevalent idea of no time in heaven comes from a misleading KJV translation of Revelation 10:6 ("there shall be time no longer"). But based on the grammar and context of that verse, it is much more likely that John meant "there would be no more delay," which is how all the modern translations render it.

Time was a part of the original perfect creation that God made for humans to live in (Gen. 1:5), so it follows that the new heavens and earth will also include that feature. But since God exists outside of time, the melding of his heaven and our earth will allow us to do that also, when God sovereignly allows it.

So I had a sense of time passing when I was in the IS, but I was also able to transcend it. And, in fact, according to God's plan for my trip, all of my adventures beyond my initial introductions actually took place in the past. (I didn't see anything in the future, but that may be possible for other creatures in heaven.)

Jesus himself sent me out on those adventures when I met him face to face in my sheath, which is what I call the temporary body I mentioned before. I won't relate the very personal matters we talked about after he told me to rise up from the prone position I had immediately assumed, and would have remained in forever if he hadn't interrupted my abject combination of remorse and praise with an embrace. But I will tell you about his commissioning of me at the end of our time together. Its progression was very much like what happened when I first arrived in heaven, and what happened to both Isaiah and Peter—a debilitating sense of unworthiness, followed by an even more intense relief and joy, concluding with a call to service.

I didn't say "Here I am, send me" like Isaiah, and Jesus didn't say "I will make you a fisher of men" as he did to Peter. But what we did say was along the same lines. I'll try to recall it as best I can, but remember that we didn't speak English in heaven (even when I had a mouth), and my experiences were so overwhelming, both in that encounter and later, that my memory is fuzzy about much of what happened. I won't use quotation marks for anything because of that limitation and the very different nature of communication there... but when I'm pretty sure about the wording, I'll represent it in a dialogue format.

I asked Jesus if I could keep worshiping him, and he said yes, but added that worship is more than just praise and singing. He said there were things he wanted me to do, and my faithfulness in them would yield a "great reward" for me in the end. He said this twice during the conversation, calling it a "blessing" the second time. (These are the most equivalent words I can manage.) I assumed at the time he meant a reward or blessing in heaven, because I thought I would be staying there. I never could have guessed then what he really meant.

He said that I would merely be an observer at the beginning (a hint at something else I never would have imagined), because I needed to get my sea legs in this new realm of existence (or "heaven legs," we could say) and learn more first before I could move on to further service.

If you're surprised to hear that we'll still be learning things in heaven, you shouldn't be. There's nothing in the Bible that says we will become omniscient when we get there—merely that we'll know much more than we do now. Only God knows everything anyway, and the Creator/creature distinction is more obvious than ever in heaven. Because of that distinction, 1 Corinthians 13:12 can't mean we'll know everything when it says, "Now I know in part; then I shall know fully, even as I have been fully known." The words before that verse introduce a *comparative* metaphor about the difference between looking at mirrors, which were made of metal back then, and looking directly at people's faces. Besides, I don't think that verse is talking about heaven at all…taken in context, I think it's about the difference between the completed canon of Scripture and the partial knowledge provided by revelatory gifts like prophecy, tongues, and words of knowledge, which Paul discusses in the surrounding chapters. (That's not a "direct revelation" I got from above, by the way. It's just my interpretation, so it could be wrong.)

To help me get accustomed to missions like this, Jesus told me I would be accompanied by the saints

I've named Jeff and Steve, the "spirits of righteous men made perfect" whom I'd met shortly after I arrived. We could also call them "ministering spirits," which brings me to another thing about the heavenly realm that might surprise you: the non-human spirit beings we call "angels" are not the only ones who visit earth, involve themselves with human affairs, and do battle with Satan and his minions. Believers who have passed into the IS do those things as well.

In case you find that difficult to believe, you should know that the words translated "angel" in the biblical languages (Hebrew *malak*, Greek *angelos*) simply mean "messenger," and there is no exegetical reason they must only refer to the non-human spirits God created. They can sometimes include human spirits as well, which is made clear by passages like Acts 12:15, where the puzzled disciples said "It is his angel" when Peter appeared at the door when he was supposed to be in prison. They thought his human spirit had come back from the dead, and they called it "his angel" (*angelos*).

I asked Jesus why he chose Jeff and Steve in particular to accompany me, and whether it was because of their sordid past. (I asked such questions boldly, because learning is not just allowed in heaven, it's encouraged.) I'd already heard from them about what they were before their conversions, and was thinking that Jesus may have picked them to drive home the point that citizenship and privilege in heaven is entirely the result of sovereign grace. But his answer was another surprise, on several fronts...

I give them some of the most special assignments, he said, because they love me so much.

I was a bit puzzled by this at the time (yes, we can be puzzled in heaven—it's part of the continuing learning process), and I didn't pursue it further. But I thought later of what Jesus had implied to a Pharisee during his earthly ministry, that our love for him is proportional to how much we've been forgiven, or at least how much we know we've been forgiven (see Luke 7:47). I also wondered about what made my "assignments" so special, because I could tell by then that this sort of thing happens all the time in the IS. But now I realize that it was because of the uniqueness of me returning and reporting what I experienced. That happens far less than you would think by looking at the bestseller charts and Christian talk shows.

The Lord was right when he said that visiting earth as a disembodied soul would take some getting used to. I wasn't wearing a sheath on my first three or four visits to the past, because I was merely observing and needed to be invisible to the humans involved. But without eyes and ears and smell and touch, my perspective on the things of earth was so different that I was somewhat disoriented throughout most of the first few trips.

Traveling through time wasn't as disorienting, however. It was more like stepping sideways, as I had described my passing into the IS, and I didn't miss our modern conveniences because my soul wasn't dependent on any of them. And though by all rights I should have been rendered catatonic by the sudden avalanche of information this new state afforded (I could "hear" some people's thoughts and "see" spiritual battles, for example), I was experiencing more awe than anxiety because what I knew and didn't know was clearly determined by a divine plan and controlled by a divine hand. I won't keep repeating this over and over again as I continue my account, but it was one of the most perpetually obvious features of the IS, and all of my adventures in it, that God gave me just enough knowledge to fulfill his purposes, but never enough to drive me mad—which I think would have easily occurred without his providential control. (I'm now convinced he does the same for us at all times on this side of heaven also, but it's just not as obvious here as it is over there.)

The star of my first visit to the past was a woman named Mae, and later ones involved two other special ladies, Elizabeth and Elsie. I know now who these women are, and why they're significant, but at the time of my trips that information was withheld from me, as were the names of others involved, so I'll leave them out here. I want to recount all this to you as it happened, so you can share in the excitement of my later discoveries.

Chapter 6

Lightning Strike

Mae had lost both her parents when she was twelve and fourteen, a fact which the devil reminded her of often, tempting her to self-pity and excuses for disobeying and ignoring God. So without any significant concern for the Lord's will, as she lived most of her young life, she married an up-and-coming young accountant, and bore him eight children over the next seventeen years.

I learned all this and more watching her sit in a church pew on Mother's Day in 1923, the first place and time Jeff and Steve took me to. It was fitting for it to be my first, because I got to witness the greatest thing that ever happens on this planet. Mae was "born again" on that day, and seeing it from my new perspective truly gave the term new meaning.

There were travails to this spiritual birth as intense as any of the eight baby deliveries that God used to make that particular day special in her mind, and to open her heart to the preaching of the Word. Several evil spirits, who had been gloating over the hypocrisy of certain church members and trying to distract others, suddenly turned their attention to Mae when a form of spiritual light or energy began to take shape around and in her. Remember, I'm doing my best here to describe things that are really indescribable to people who have not experienced that realm of reality. But for the sake of my story, and because you'll hear more about this later, I'll borrow some terms from a fantasy novel I once read and say that the power transforming Mae that morning was a combination of God's *bara-pneuma* and his *asah-pneuma*. The first is the creative power of His Spirit (the person of the Trinity who interacts most directly with our universe), and the second is his "working" power.

The flower-like bloom inside and surrounding Mae was the Holy Spirit creating a new person with a new nature within her, as she repented of her sins and trusted in the promise of the gospel for forgiveness and new life.

It's no accident that 1 John 3:9 uses an implantation metaphor when it says, "No one born of God makes a practice of sinning, for God's seed abides in him; and he cannot keep on sinning, because he has been born of God." And part and parcel of Mae's conversion, because of the new spiritual life within her, was a commitment to obey God's commands like she never had before.

Unfortunately (or the opposite, depending on how you look at it), that new commitment to obedience sounded the death knell of her marriage.

The next time and place we visited was the home of Mae and her husband in September of 1923, and by then their relationship had deteriorated considerably, as was obvious by the conversation we witnessed. It went something like this...

You *cannot* keep doing what you're doing to those clients of yours, Mae said. It's not right.

I told you, it's part of the business, her husband answered.

Not according to God. He said "Thou shalt not steal."

It's different than stealing. I told you we will not be talking about this anymore.

Then I might have to talk to them about it.

You wouldn't dare, he spat at her. That wouldn't only lose me one of my biggest accounts, it would ruin my reputation.

I have to do what God says.

You don't have to do anything. God isn't telling you anything. You're sick in the head. God never talks to me.

He does in the Scriptures, Mae said. But you don't listen to him.

I've had enough of your holier-than-thou religion. Stop talking about this, or… you'll regret it!

Mae didn't stop. Her conscience must have continued to plague her severely—perhaps because she knew the client family that her husband was taking advantage of? She wrote a letter to them, and the letter somehow ended up in the hands of a local newspaper reporter. The reporter, sensing a possible scandal, was less than discreet when he interviewed Mae's husband and let on that Mae had written the letter. Her husband demanded to see it, and then, enraged at her and the children (who defended her), and despondent about his future business prospects, he left them all and moved into the city to live by himself.

In December 1923, he wrote out an addendum to his will and delivered it to his lawyer. Cutting Mae and all their children out, it said that all his possessions should go to his sister and brother-in-law, because "they have proven themselves my friends." The hand-written note concluded in this way: "I have done the best I have known how, but that seems not enough to please the world. I therefore leave it with no regrets and with no malice in my heart toward those who have brought about this end."

In April of the next year, he filed for divorce on the grounds of libel. He didn't do much to advance the case over the next few years because he was too busy enjoying the single life in the city and trying to build a new clientele there, and the litigation remained inert. But Mae had to care for eight children all by herself, earning money here and there when she could and wondering every month whether they would have food and shelter for the next one.

Four years later, in January 1928, the estranged husband started returning to their home town periodically and telling Mae and the children he was going to build a house for them all on some property he owned. Apparently his business in the city had failed, so he sold a rental house he had purchased elsewhere to return to the area and live off the connections he still had there. To do this, he needed to be enough of a respectable family man to gain the trust of the rural, highly religious natives, and that was his main reason for re-unifying his family in the house he was building. He also withdrew the divorce/libel action that had been lingering in the courts. New house, new marriage, "new man"—he thought that would get him enough customers to sustain his business there.

These motives were apparent to me as we listened to another conversation between the couple, in August of 1928. They sat on a picnic bench while several of the younger children played nearby.

When the house is finished, he said, we'll all move in there together, except there will be enough rooms for you and me to each have our own.

Why bother if we are not to live as man and wife? Mae asked.

I have my reasons.

Are any of them God's will? Do you care at all about what he wants?

You know I'm a Christian man. I've always been a Christian. If you want me to return you mustn't judge me.

If you return without repenting of your sins, you'll only make life even harder for me and the children.

You can pray for me, he said with frustrated sarcasm.

I do pray for you, Mae answered. In my desperation I've prayed that God will convert you or take you home. That's how serious this is.

Take me…what do you mean by that? I'll get struck by lightning for blaspheming God? He rolled his eyes and waved his hands in the air mockingly.

He could do that, Mae said. While you're working on the house one day, if you're not building it for the right reasons.

Oh Mae, you're such a fool. We never even work when there's a storm, on account of all the metal equipment. You're a fool.

As he waved her off and began to leave the table, I could tell that Mae was thinking of telling him that according to Jesus, anyone who calls someone a fool is deserving of the fires of hell. (Some thoughts I could "hear" and others I could not, as I said, at the discretion of God's all-controlling providence.) But she restrained herself—something she was learning and practicing to do more in preparation for living with an unbelieving husband again. Instead, she simply sent up another prayer that if it was God's will, he would either change him or take him away before she had to endure that eventuality.

Their youngest son was one of the children playing nearby that day, and he half-listened to his parents' conversation after his interest was caught by the reference to being struck by lightning. And the seven-year-old was also present at the next scene Jeff and Steve took me to, on August 22 of 1928.

Mae's husband and a few other men were working on the new house (on a clear day, of course) when the well-drilling machine he was using impacted an underground electric line, and he was killed instantly. This was a truly bizarre thing for me to witness because I could see the electricity enter his body and stop his heart (to a disembodied soul energy is nearly as visible as matter), and because his body changed so drastically from my perspective when his soul suddenly disappeared from it. But of course what was most amazing was the connection between this event and the recent conversation between him and Mae, and her prayers about him. This was not lost on their son either—in fact, his young mind was so impressed by the coincidence that he would remember it for the rest of his life. And when the police detective and the newspaper man questioned the boy after it occurred, they both left with the impression that his mother had prayed for him to be struck down by lightning.

Don't go writin' that in the paper, the detective told the newspaper man in the next conversation I was privy to. It'll get all around town and create headaches we don't wanna have.

What am I supposed to write then? The reporter asked him.

I don't know. Anything but that. And I mean it.

The headline that ended up in the paper was, "Well Known Local Man Collapses While Supervising The Sinking Well At Home." And the body of the article said that he was "Seized with an attack of acute indigestion while he was directing well digging operations at his new house," that he "had been in good health," but "was seen to fall to the ground, and by the time workmen reached his side he was breathing his last."

Acute indigestion?

Truth really is stranger than fiction.

Chapter 7

The Patriarchs

The next thing I remember was a series of events much farther back in history, which gave me the impression that all my "assignments" would be random, rather than having some connection with one another.

Steve was off on a separate mission from God, at some other place and time. But Jeff and I found ourselves looking down at a large swath of mostly barren land punctuated by a grove of large twisty trees. There were some tents set up under the trees, and others to one side of them.

And there were three figures walking side by side across the plain toward the trees and tents.

I could immediately tell they were not mere humans (spiritual qualities were more apparent in the bodiless state because we weren't seeing with physical eyes). The aura exuded by the three travelers was also noticed by a man sitting at the door of his tent under the trees, and as our souls (or at least our perspective) zoomed in closer on the scene, I recognized the man, even though he'd lived 4000 years before I was born.

I don't know whether God revealed it to my mind, or if my knowledge of Scripture informed me, but I realized that he was Abraham, the father of the Jewish people. And just as we can read in Genesis 18, he jumped up from his seat at the door of his tent, ran toward the three men as they approached, and bowed before them. It occurred to me that he also knew who they were in one of the same two ways—either from what God had revealed to him before, or by a Divine illumination "on the spot."

Regardless of how we knew, Abraham and I both had no doubt that the three men were actually the Lord, manifesting himself as human to presage the incarnation of Christ, and as three men to picture the Trinity. (When I went back and read the passage later, so many details came alive to me as never before—like how both singular and plural pronouns are used for the men, and how all three are referred to collectively as "the Lord" while remaining distinct persons.)

O Lord, Abraham said to them, if I have found favor in your sight, do not pass by your servant. Let a little water be brought, and wash your feet, and rest yourselves under the tree, while I bring a morsel of bread, that you may refresh yourselves, and after that you may pass on—since you have come to your servant.

Do as you have said, they answered.

Only one at a time was talking in the physical realm, but in a spiritual sense they all spoke.

Then Abraham ran around for a while like a chicken with his head cut off—it was like someone meeting a favorite pop star. He dashed into the tent to tell Sarah to make some cake, out to the herd nearby to order a calf to be slaughtered and cooked, and back to his lodgings to prepare some curds and milk for his visitors.

While this was going on, I studied the three-man "theophany" that had now sat down under one of the trees to wait for Abraham's meal. In my IS perception, this visible manifestation of the Godhead seemed to be pulsing with the incommunicable attributes I had learned about in my previous studies, but could never have been prepared for their reality.

Unlike any of the creation around them, and even Jeff and I in our perfected spiritual states, the three Divine persons radiated a degree self-sufficiency and satisfaction that I could never even have imagined. Also, their immutability (or "unchangeableness") was such a tangible trait that it could be felt within seconds, again especially in contrast to the bi-polar emotions and thoughts their presence was producing in Abraham and Sarah. And the attribute of omnipresence was also apparent: even though the Father, Son, and Holy Spirit were represented physically in that place, there was never any question that they were also everywhere else in the universe at the same time.

The eternality of God was also unmistakable as I observed the three men, and it wasn't just due to the fact that I was experiencing in real time something that happened thousands of years before I was born. There was also a palpable impression that these beings never had any beginning. Again, I can't explain it, because it wasn't analogous to any earthly human experience. But suffice to say that in the manifested presence of God, that attribute is as noticeable and remarkable as any other, which serves constantly (like the others) to prove how utterly different the Creator is from the creature.

And the omniscience of God was obvious in the next interaction…

When the food was fully prepared, and the three men were eating it (another prefiguring of the genuine human nature and body that Christ would take on when he later came to the earth), they asked where Sarah was.

She's in the tent, Abraham answered.

I will surely return to you about this time next year, the Lord promised, and Sarah your wife shall have a son.

After a pregnant pause (no pun intended), he added, Why did Sarah laugh when I said that, thinking she's too old to bear a child? Is anything too hard for the Lord? I'm telling you again, at the appointed time I will return to you, about this time next year, and Sarah will have a son.

I didn't laugh, Sarah said from the door of the tent, much more loudly than was necessary, considering they could hear her thoughts.

Yes, you did, said the Lord.

After that we "shifted" to another time and place, not many years later and about thirty miles away.

Abraham, along with his son Isaac and two servants, approached a hill in Moriah where God had told him to go. I immediately sensed an almost unbearable conflict in the patriarch's heart, as a plague of conflicting thoughts resounded in his mind.

God has been so good…why would he do this to me now? How could he expect me to do something that seems so wrong? I know we all deserve death for our sins, and life for any of us is a privilege of his grace, but he promised it to me and my offspring. How could a great nation come from me if my only child is gone? But I know I must trust and obey, even when I don't understand what he's doing. I believe he could raise Isaac from the dead…

Stay here with the donkey, Abraham said to the two servants at the foot of the mountain. I and the boy will go over there and worship and come again to you.

When he said that, he was again thinking that if he did what God had told him to do, Isaac could be brought back to life. So he asked his son to carry the wood for the burnt offering, while he himself held the knife and the fire materials, and they started up the slope.

Father? Isaac said along the way. I see the fire and the wood, but where is the lamb for a burnt offering?

God will provide the lamb, his father answered.

As they reached the top of the hill and prepared the altar for the sacrifice, Jeff suddenly disappeared from the scene (maybe because God wanted me to witness this without any distraction?). I immediately began to feel uneasy, and was drawn more into empathy with Abraham's tortured emotions as he tied Isaac to the altar and raised the knife…

But it was also an indescribable blessing to feel his relief when a voice from heaven called out at the last moment and stopped him from cutting his son's throat.

Do not lay your hand on the boy or do anything to him, the voice said, for now I know that you fear God, seeing you have not withheld your son, your only son, from me.

My presentation of dialog in this book may not always be precise, but I do remember very specifically, as reflected in Genesis 22, that "the angel of the Lord" who spoke to Abraham in that situation also referred to himself as the Lord ("you have not withheld your only son *from me*"). So like in other cases in the Old Testament when the definite article is used ("*the* angel of the Lord"), this was Jesus Christ himself, in another pre-incarnate theophany, who appeared to Abraham. That makes the several references to "your son, your only son" all the more meaningful.

Abraham saw a ram caught by his horns in a bush nearby, which he then offered up as a burnt offering instead of his son. So he named the place Yahweh Yirah (*Jehovah-Jireh* in Latin), which means "The Lord will provide." And in commemoration his people would later be known to recite, "On the mount of the Lord it shall be provided."

About a thousand years later Solomon would build and dedicate his temple on that same mountain, in the middle of a city called Jerusalem. And a thousand years after that the promised Messiah would be crucified there.

I wondered at that moment why God had not sent me on a trip to that most important moment in history (the Cross), but then I realized that its memory was always in our minds while we were in the IS. It permeated the very atmosphere we lived in and was always as close at hand as any other thought, because it was the only reason we had all the blessings we were enjoying.

I was still alone when I was whisked away to a final

event in the lives of the patriarchs—this one involving Abraham's grandson Jacob. Maybe it was because Jacob himself was alone that night, and God wanted me to empathize again. He had sent his family to the other side of the river, and was filled with fear because a formidable army led by his brother Esau was pursuing and about to overtake him. This was the brother, you might remember, whom Jacob had swindled out of his birthright by taking advantage of him in a weak moment and then impersonating him to deceive their father Isaac.

By allowing me to see Jacob's thoughts that night as he remembered those and many other sins he had committed, God clearly wanted me to know how undeserving he was. In fact, Jacob struggled in vain to remember anything he had ever done that was truly praiseworthy, which is reflected in the Old Testament texts about him. Other than praying for and blessing his children at the very end of his life, Jacob never does anything very good in the biblical accounts. (And that end-of-life exception is the only thing said about him when he's mentioned in the "Hall of Faith" in Hebrews 11.)

When I arrived on the scene, Jacob and another man were rolling around on the ground in a struggle (the Hebrew term for "wrestling" comes from the word for dust). The other figure had the same spiritual "glow" as the three men Abraham met with in the earlier story and is referred to in Scripture as both "the angel of the Lord" and God Himself.

So it was Jesus Christ whom Jacob encountered that night. But instead of worshiping the eternal Son of

God as he should have, Jacob ended up in a fight with him! The fact that it was a fight was clear to me when witnessing it, and I've checked the story in Genesis 32 to confirm it. Other verses in that passage make clear that the "wrestling" was more than a mere sport—for example, it says in verse 28 that Jacob had been "striving" with God, and in verse 30 he is surprised that he even survived the encounter.

I didn't see how the battle began, but I got to see how it ended. When Jacob wouldn't give up after a long period of time, Jesus finally stopped the conflict by dislocating the patriarch's hip with a mere touch. But even incapacitated from the waist down, the desperate sinner clung to Christ and said, "I won't let go until you bless me."

In a way Jacob *was* doing something admirable here—not in the sense of "good works" as we normally think of them, because he should have been bowing before Jesus rather than striving with him. But the patriarch did recognize that he had nothing to offer the Lord except his own neediness, and that the mercy of Christ was his only hope for deliverance and blessing. In that moment he reminded me of the tax collector Jesus would later describe in Luke 18:9-14, whose faith also took the form of physical and verbal desperation when he "beat his breast" and said "God, be merciful to me, a sinner!"

So Jacob was not a hero in any typical sense—contending with God is not a good thing, remember—but the fact that his only hope and trust was in God's mercy, and that he was truly desperate for it, brought him the blessing he desired.

What is your name? Jesus said to him.

Jacob.

Your name will no longer be called Jacob, but Israel, for you have striven with God and with men, and have prevailed.

It was obvious watching all this that Jacob's "prevailing" did not mean he won the fight, or otherwise earned the right to be the father and namesake of all God's people from then on. He "prevailed" or overcame simply because God was being gracious and merciful to him. And that's what amazes me about the story, in the context of all the bad things Jacob had done and his utter inability to save himself from the destruction that was approaching in the form of Esau's army: the man who received the name "Israel," and therefore became a representative for all of God's chosen people, did nothing to deserve that blessing. All he did was believe.

Then Jacob asked him, "Please tell me your name."

But the Lord said, "Why is it that you ask my name?"

And then he blessed him.

Before I had time to ponder any possible connections between the various events I'd witnessed, I found myself back in heaven, participating in the only proper response to such amazing grace—a heavenly "worship service" for the God of Abraham, Isaac, and Jacob.

Instead of trying to describe what happened then, and a number of other times while I was in the IS, I'll let Revelation 4 tell you what it was like. That passage contains a vision that John was given of some corporate worship in heaven—he did not experience it himself like I did, but his inspired metaphorical words capture its essence and transcendence better than I could with my own...

I was in the Spirit, and behold, a throne stood in heaven, with one seated on the throne. And he who sat there had the appearance of jasper and carnelian, and around the throne was a rainbow that had the appearance of an emerald. Around the throne were twenty-four thrones, and seated on the thrones were twenty-four elders, clothed in white garments, with golden crowns on their heads. From the throne came flashes of lightning, and rumblings and peals of thunder, and before the throne were burning seven torches of fire, which are the seven spirits of God, and before the throne there was as it were a sea of glass, like crystal.

And around the throne, on each side of the throne, are four living creatures, full of eyes in front and behind: the first living creature like a lion, the second living creature like an ox, the third living creature with the face of a man, and the fourth living creature like an eagle in flight. And the four living creatures, each of them with six wings, are full of eyes all around and within, and day and night they never cease to say, "Holy, holy, holy, is the Lord God Almighty, who was and is and is to come!"

And whenever the living creatures give glory and honor and thanks to him who is seated on the throne, who lives forever and ever, the twenty-four elders fall down before him who is seated on the throne and worship him who lives forever and ever. They cast their crowns before the throne, saying, "Worthy are you, our Lord and God, to receive glory and honor and power, for you created all things, and by your will they existed and were created."

Chapter 8

The Two Charleses

At some point toward the end of that prolonged time of (literally) heavenly worship, when my soul felt satisfied like my body does after a great meal, Jesus drew me near to him, smiled warmly (and somewhat mischievously it seemed), and sent me back in time again.

In this next adventure I was alone from the beginning, with no Jeff or Steve, and my initial vantage point followed a polished horse-drawn carriage down a lane to a large house that seemed slightly familiar to me. I could tell it was a dark night, even though the light from the oil lamps and candles on the property were exaggerated in my eyeless spiritual sight.

As were the menagerie of good and evil spirits that hovered near the stocky, bearded man who exited the coach—unbeknownst to him of course. He stepped up to the front door and was met there by a somewhat portly middle-aged woman who said, "Welcome to Gad's Hill Place, Mr. Spurgeon. Mr. Dickens is waiting for you in the library."

If I'd had a mouth and lungs, I would have gasped. But as it were, my metaphorical head started spinning, and I began conversing with Jesus in my mind, which

I could do at any time. (We can do that during our earthly lives as well, of course, but our awareness of the privilege is much stronger in the IS.)

Were Spurgeon and Dickens actually friends? I asked. *I thought they never met…at least it was never recorded that they did, right?*

This was the only time, the Lord answered, his words accompanied by a palpable sense of pride and joy. *It's a meeting no one knew about on June 7, 1870, two days before Dickens died.*

I was too much in shock to "move" my own soul into the house, but thank God an unseen hand guided me there. I won't be able to remember and record all the exact words the two men said to one another, except for some of the related facts and written excerpts that I was able to find in the historical record. But suffice to say that the words they spoke in conversation were almost as brilliant as those that can be read in print. I doubt that anyone was ever more gifted with the English language, or any language for that matter, other than Christ and the writings inspired by his Spirit. So there is no way I can fully capture their eloquence, but again I'll do my feeble best.

I hope you didn't mind being greeted by my sister-in-law Georgina, Dickens said when she ushered Spurgeon into his library, which was lined floor-to-ceiling by books on two sides, and by three large windows on another. Under the middle window sat a formidable desk, and above the author himself floated apparitions—not of his many characters like in the painting called "Dickens' Dream," but more of the good and bad spirits that had accompanied his guest.

Apparently this was not just a unique meeting of two of the world's most famous men, but an important event in the spiritual realm also. Or maybe the forces of good and evil were always hard at work around both of them.

I sent the servants away tonight, Dickens continued, because I cannot necessarily trust them to keep confidence. Georgina, however, is quite discreet.

I could tell that Spurgeon reacted to this in his mind, thinking something to the effect of "I'm sure she is," but not saying anything. He didn't want to turn his new acquaintance off at the very beginning of their meeting by hinting at the reports of the mistress who allegedly had ruined his marriage. (Although most of the rumors swirled around a young actress named Ellen Tiernan, there had also been some less likely suspicions about Georgina, who since the separation had kept Dickens' house and cared for his ten children.)

Dickens, for his part, was only thinking this about Spurgeon: *He's shorter than I expected.*

I found even this partial insight into the men's thoughts distracting, and wanted to enjoy this visit as much as possible, so I asked the Lord to "turn them off." He did, and from then on I could only hear their words.

Should I call you Reverend? Dickens asked, ushering the preacher to a chair across from his. You don't seem to be the type for such… affectations.

I'm not, the burly younger man replied. You can call me Charles.

Wonderful. And you can call *me* Charles.

Fast friends, Spurgeon said with a wry smile.

And strange bedfellows? Dickens responded.

Perhaps not as strange as one might have thought, Spurgeon suggested, then pulled a note out of his pocket and held it up like a specimen.

This invitation from you asks if I remember three recent donations of one thousand pounds each for our ministries, from an anonymous donor who had given only the initials A. B. So you either know the donor, or you are the donor.

Please forgive the intrigue, Dickens said. 'Twas the only way I could assure you'd come tonight. From what I heard, those gifts arrived at a time of great need, so I was confident you'd want to express your appreciation in person.

Great need is an understatement, my friend. The construction of our fledgling orphanage was halted until we received that first generous gift, and the second bank note from A. B. that arrived two weeks later put us ahead of schedule. You cannot imagine the rejoicing and praise to God, not to mention relief, those gifts solicited from our board and staff.

I'm gratified, the famous author said, after a slightly embarrassed pause.

I've had only the ride over here to make some guesses at the meaning of the initials our anonymous donor chose.

Oh? What do you suppose?

"Anonymous Benefactor" is the odds-on favorite, Spurgeon answered. Or "Admiring Benefactor" perhaps. Or Angelo Bantam, the Master of Ceremonies from *The Pickwick Papers*…

I'm surprised that such an heir of the Puritans has

a knowledge of gambling parlance, and I'm even more impressed that you would remember the name of a minor character from one of my novels.

I remember everything I read, Spurgeon said, simply as a matter of fact, and with no visible pride. So what does A. B. stand for?

Hmmm. I'm afraid you think me too clever. I simply picked the first two letters of the alphabet, seeing as the third and fourth might have given me away.

Both men laughed, and each did so with obvious sincerity. Even without the ability to read their minds or hearts, I could tell that neither was interested in making a show on this occasion.

Speaking of *Pickwick*, Spurgeon added, I've often said that my assistant George, whose given name is John L. Keys, reminds me of Sam Weller from that story. He certainly has many quaint sayings which that worthy might have uttered. You'd like him.

I'm sure I would, Dickens said, and then grimaced from some kind of physical pain that was plaguing him.

So the donations *were* from your hand.

Yes, Dickens admitted. Though I'd be obliged if you kept that between us.

I certainly will, for I am the one obliged. I can't help but wonder at it, however. I never would have thought you to be an ally of mine.

And I was not, until recently, when I found my mind to be opened.

Why? Spurgeon asked.

Why was my mind opened, or why was I not an admirer of yours?

The latter first.

Well, for one, your brand of Calvinism has always brought a particular stench to my nostrils. No pun intended.

Perhaps because you don't understand it rightly.

Also, many of the... heirs of the Puritans, we'll call them, are more-than-easy targets for my satire of religious hypocrisy. The shoe fits with all too many of you, I'm afraid. And you preach against the theater, which is actually my first love.

I understand now why you were not an ally, Spurgeon said, but I find it surprising that you did not become a public enemy by pointing your satirical bow in my direction.

You've always seemed different, more worthy of respect, though not quite enough to escape your associations. Why have you not criticized *me* publicly?

For the same reason, though not quite enough to allay the suspicions.

Ah, Dickens sighed, the persistent gossip about my domestic difficulties. One thing I've learned in life is that no one but yourself will ever understand some things that befall you. I am not a perfect man by any means, but I assure you I am not as hideously monstrous as I am made out to be.

I'm not inclined to disagree with you, the preacher said. I myself don't happen to be as uncivil and judgmental as some think. People often tell me that I'm more pleasant in person than in my sermons.

But you seem to have thoroughly avoided the kinds of scandal that always seems to plague great men, whether deserved or not. Rather you are notorious for your devotion to an invalid wife.

All glory to God, Spurgeon said. But I do often fail to love her as I should.

A moment of silence passed between the two men, indicating that they had reached the end of any mutual discussion of the famous author's marital troubles. At least for now.

Then Spurgeon asked, When did your mind open to the idea that I might not be a hypocrite like all the others?

When you announced that you were opening an orphanage in the vein of the Ragged Schools, which I have always supported.

And a third bank note designated for my Pastors College, Spurgeon said, was delivered with the second donation to the orphanage, accompanied by a note saying, "The latter led me to contribute to the former."

Yes, Dickens said. If you are able to seed the world with other men who will do the work you're doing, that may not be so bad after all, despite some of what you're teaching them. I also became aware that you've been including leaders and teachers from other denominations in your various ministries, and that clears you from another great fault I find with ministers of your ilk.

Well, now that we've almost established our mutual admiration society, Spurgeon grinned again, why did you invite me to come tonight?

I wanted to ask you some questions, but I was shy of sending a letter.

Yes, I understand you are given to burn them.

Dickens grimaced again, this time with a pain

that wasn't physical, and I wondered why his guest would be so rude as to break the unspoken policy of silence about the writer's possible infidelity. But then it occurred to me that Spurgeon may have been emulating the way Jesus related to the woman at the well in John 4, when he asked her to go get her husband and did not allow himself to be diverted from the issue of her illicit relationships. Or this Baptist preacher may have felt conscience-bound to follow in the footsteps of John the Baptist, who was not intimidated in the presence of Herod the Great and refused to be silent about the King's affair with his sister-in-law. Or maybe Spurgeon just imitated Jesus and John unconsciously, because he was so steeped in the Scriptures, and "if pricked would bleed Bibline," as he liked to say about his hero John Bunyan.

Speaking of correspondence, Dickens said, clearing his throat in an attempt to both shake off his pain and redirect the conversation, This is what I wanted to ask you about.

He pulled two letters off his desk and held one out to Spurgeon.

I received this today from the Reverend John M. Makeham, Dickens explained, whose name I will refrain from mocking or using in one of my stories. As you can see, he takes exception to a sentence in the latest serialized chapter of *Edwin Drood*. Seems he thinks I was plagiarizing—and disparaging in some way—a passage from the Old Testament book of Isaiah. He implies that I was blaspheming our Lord, and since he is a Non-Conformist minister, I thought you could understand him better than I, and advise me.

I don't even conform to the Non-Comformists, Spurgeon said without looking up from his perusal of the letter, but I will be glad to help in any way I can.

I fear that I am not long for this world, Dickens said, and I'd prefer to not leave it in the midst of a religious controversy that could have been avoided. *Drood* might be my last work, and I'm afraid I may not even be able to finish it.

I'm sorry to hear about your health, Spurgeon said with genuine sympathy, meeting the writer's damp eyes. But then a small smile bent his lips ever-so-slightly, and he added, Will you tell us how it ends?

It seemed to me that Spurgeon was not only a great preacher and leader, but also a good judge of personality. Far from being offended at this light-hearted spit in death's eye, the legendary author actually warmed to it.

Not a chance, Dickens answered. My readers will have much more fun with it if they don't know. The Boz's art has always imitated his mysterious life, and will continue to do so in death.

Dickens held out the response letter he had written to the Reverend Makeham, and said that Spurgeon should read what he had so far. The preacher took one look at the handwriting, however, and suggested that Dickens read it for him. This produced some more chuckles from both men.

Dear Sir, Dickens began, it would be quite inconceivable I think—but for your letter—that any reasonable reader could possibly attach a scriptural reference to a passage in a book of mine, reproducing a much abused social figure of speech, impressed into all sorts of service on all sorts of inappropriate occasions, without the faintest connexion of it with its original source. I am truly shocked to find that any reader can make the mistake. I have always striven in my writings to express veneration for the life and lessons of our Saviour; because I feel it; and because I re-wrote that history for my children—every one of whom knew it from having it repeated to them—long before they could read, and almost as soon as they could speak.

What do you think? Dickens asked when he was done. Will this mollify Mr. Makeham and keep me from being dragged through the mud as a heretic among you, more than I've already been, that is?

Well, Spurgeon replied, this Reverend might not recognize a metaphor if it bit him on the leg, but I think he will be more or less satisfied by the second half of the letter. You should not be so critical of him, however, because you bear some responsibility for his misapprehension of your words.

How so?

You have not been clear and forthright enough in your profession of faith, especially in light of all your lampooning of religion. Even the book about Christ's life that you mention, which you wrote for your children, has never been released to the public.

Bah! the inventor of Ebenezer Scrooge said, and I half-expected him to add "Humbug!" I've written other letters like this, I wish you could see them. But all right, I have ears to hear...

Dickens swung his wheeled chair around, grabbed a pen, and grunted as he added one more line to the end of the letter, before signing it and folding it up.

(Later I found out what he wrote, because the letter still exists today. It says, "But I have never made proclamation of this from the house tops." I also noticed, as Spurgeon did, how bad his handwriting was in the days prior to his death.)

When Dickens turned back to face his guest, Spurgeon sat quietly staring at him. A few moments of silence passed between the two men, and then the younger one broke it.

There must be another reason you brought me here, he said. Something more grave than that letter. You haven't even offered me a drink or a cigar.

Dickens continued neglecting those practices of hospitality and looked at the floor for a few more pregnant moments. Then he spun around again and retrieved a document from a drawer in his desk.

This is my last will and testament, he said, drafted last year. You shall tell me whether I've made a good end. I have wondered if I should modify it.

I sensed that Spurgeon was now starting to recognize the nature of this pastoral call, and I was too.

The handwriting was much better on the will, having been done by an attorney, so the preacher took it and read it as Dickens looked on, shifting occasionally in his seat from pain or nervousness or both.

Whether or not you've made a good end to your life, Spurgeon said when he handed the will back to Dickens, is between you and the Lord. I cannot, nor can any man, be your judge in private matters such as your relationship with your wife and the other women you mention, unless you want to share more with me about that. But I can say that you made a good end to the document itself.

What do you mean?

Read the second-to-last sentence aloud, like a prayer.

"I commit my soul to the mercy of God through our Lord and Savior Jesus Christ, and I exhort my dear children humbly to try to guide themselves by the teaching of the New Testament in its broad spirit, and to put no faith in any man's narrow construction of its letter here or there." Do you believe that my disdain for denominations and theological arguments is…worthy of damnation?

Perhaps, Spurgeon answered with another wry smile. As all errors of doctrine are…even my own, whatever they may be. But you seem to have a desire for honor and obedience to God's Word, however deficient your understanding of it. Are you repentant for your own sins?

There are many, ah, complexities that prevent me from knowing exactly what has and has not been "sin" in my life, as you call it. I am a novelist, remember, not a priest. But I *am* sorry for whatever I've done wrong, what I know and what I do not.

It may be that you have not knowingly repented for every sin you've committed, Spurgeon observed, and you might not have produced all the commensurate fruits of repentance. I can only enjoin you to do so. But that leads us to the first clause of the excerpt… read that again.

"I commit my soul to the mercy of God through our Lord and Savior Jesus Christ."

Ahhh, Spurgeon said. If that is truly the posture

of your heart, I believe you can be confident of your justification and acceptance before God, regardless of how perfectly you've repented or done anything else. I am not your confessor, nor can I absolve you or grant you assurance—only the Lord can do that. But I gladly admit that I find myself encouraged by the fact that your "last words" sound more like the tax collector than the Pharisee.

As there was another pause in the conversation, I noticed for the first time that the evil spirits had cleared out from the scene, and only elect angels were attending now. I didn't know whether this meant that Dickens was being converted or comforted, because the state of his soul was not apparent to me, or if the power of gospel truth had simply caused the darkness to flee. I found myself deeply hoping for the former.

Would you pray for me? Dickens said with tears in his eyes, though again I could not tell their cause, whether it was joy or regret or both.

I would love to, Spurgeon said, and took the writer's hands in his as he bowed.

Our Father, Thou dost hear us when we pray. Thou hast provided an advocate and intercessor in heaven now; we cannot come to Thee unless Thy Holy Spirit shall suggest desire, and help us while we plead. We would ask that the subject which caused such conflict to Paul may be beyond conflict with us; may we know the Christ and have Him to be our all in all. We would have the conflict about others, but may we be past it for ourselves.

Lord God the Holy Ghost, may faith grow in my friend Charles; may he believe in Christ to the saving of his soul. May his little faith brighten into strong faith, and may his strong faith ripen into the full assurance of faith. Resting in the Great Surety and High Priest of the New Covenant, may he feel "the peace of God which passeth all understanding," and may he enter into rest.

May he not place his trust in his own good works of promoting charity for the poor, nor seek to excuse his sins by thinking he is not as corrupt as other men. May he not rely upon any words of mine, even the words of this prayer, but in Thy Word, oh God—the only sure foundation upon which to build our house of faith. May these solemn words, which he has immortalized in his writing, arise in his mind as he travels down the dark streets, among the heavy shadows: "I am the resurrection and the life, saith the Lord: he that believeth in me, though he were dead, yet shall he live: and whosoever liveth and believeth in me, shall never die."

May this prayer that had broken up out of his heart for a merciful consideration of all his poor blindnesses and errors, end in the words, "I am the resurrection and the life." In his twilight may the substance of the shadow be apparent to him, may he take joy in the many lives that will be touched by the Divine truth he has put down, despite his sins and errors, and may he give Thee glory for any blessing that Thou mayest bestow through him.

May he be able to say, in a humble faith that I hope and pray resides in his heart, "It is a far, far better thing that I do, than I have ever done; it is a far, far better rest that I go to than I have ever known." Amen.

Spurgeon opened his eyes and raised his head, to see Dickens staring open mouthed at him. The second half of the prayer had been filled with direct quotes from the end of *A Tale of Two Cities*.

I told you, the preacher said, I remember everything I read.

Charles Dickens sent out the response letter to the Reverend Makeham the next morning, spent the afternoon writing the next part of *The Mystery of Edwin Drood*, and suffered a massive stroke at dinner time, entering into a state of unconsciousness from which he would never recover. He died the next day.

The response to Makeham was Dickens' final letter, and on the last page he ever wrote (in the *Drood* manuscript) there is a funeral scene described in this way:

> A brilliant morning shines on the old city. Its antiquities and ruins are surpassingly beautiful, with a lusty ivy gleaming in the sun, and the rich trees waving in the balmy air. Changes of glorious light from moving boughs, songs of birds, scents from gardens, woods, and fields—or, rather, from the one great garden of the whole cultivated island in its yielding time—penetrate into the Cathedral, subdue its earthy odour, and preach the Resurrection and the Life. The cold stone tombs of centuries ago grow warm; and flecks of brightness dart into the sternest marble corners of the building, fluttering there like wings.

Chapter 9

Nervous Breakdown

My next visit to the past was to a time much later than the Victorian age in England, and back to America again. But this time the people were unrecognizable to me again. I met a remarkable woman named Elizabeth, but had no idea who she was until much later. Perhaps I could have figured it out earlier if I had applied myself more, but I was too disoriented from the wide variety of people and times I was experiencing to see any connection between them and anyone I knew.

The Great Depression in the United States had led to a nagging depression in Elizabeth's husband. From the interaction I witnessed in the winter of 1939, I could tell that he had been agonizing and complaining for a long time about the difficulties of providing for a growing family. And when he walked upstairs threatening to kill himself after a particularly difficult day, Elizabeth followed him just in case he was really serious. The distraught man opened a second-story window and stretched his leg out over the sill, while his wife tugged on him and begged him to stop.

More importantly, though, she was begging God to stop him. And as she prayed, one of my guides intervened on her behalf. It would be impossible to describe this satisfactorily to you, because of the wide differences between the physical and spiritual realms, so I'll more or less just tell you what happened. Steve entered into a battle with two demons that were afflicting Elizabeth's husband and managed to beat them back long enough to give the depressed man some respite, and restrain his self-destructive impulses long enough to keep him from jumping.

This was the first direct evidence I had of human souls participating in spiritual battles on earth—remember what I told you earlier about the word "angel"—and I learned later that Steve was given this privilege because during his life he had been suicidal, yet delivered from that fate by one of God's people. His intense joy at being able to save the man's life in response to Elizabeth's prayers was contagious and made me want to experience it myself.

(As a side note, seeing this metaphysical drama play out was interesting to me when I remembered how puzzled I had been during my first life about the relationship between God's sovereignty and human choices. In this situation there was no doubt that God himself was responding to Elizabeth's prayers and controlling everything that happened, while at the same time allowing Steve the privilege of participating in his work. And this concurrence of Divine and human action brought equal joy to both parties—in heaven there is no conflict between those two dynamics.)

After her husband agreed to leave the window and try to get some rest, Elizabeth's thoughts conducted their own battle with one another.

He needs help that he's not getting through the church, she thought. *The pastor and the other board members have advised him, but it hasn't worked. Maybe it's their fault, or maybe his for not following their counsel. So he needs medical help.*

But both they and he himself have always said the psychiatrists and mental wards are the devil's way of solving problems. If he goes there they will judge him, and he probably won't be able to live with himself.

Oh Lord, she cried out in her mind, since she never had too many thoughts without them turning to God, *what should I do? Should I call the men in white suits or not? I can't take much more of this, the children can't either, and he'll hurt himself and leave us all alone...*

She went on back and forth like this for a long time, and then, in the absence of any direct response to her prayers, she made the kind of tough decision that Mae had made when she sent that letter to the family being disadvantaged by her husband. Elizabeth went downstairs, picked up the phone, and started the process of having hers committed.

We saw glimpses of the following weeks, when he was carted off resignedly to a state hospital and the children were farmed out so that Elizabeth herself could recover (from both his problems and the trauma of her difficult choice). We saw some demons laugh over him while he received shock therapy in that horrific place, and we saw others flee from Elizabeth when she persevered in prayer. We saw how his fellow leaders in the church refused to visit him in the hospital, and then how one of them implied that he was marked for life with the equivalent of a "Scarlet A" because he went to "the world" for help with his problems, rather than to God.

I'm not sure whether the man who spoke to him really meant to suggest that, but that's how he took it, as one of the demons watching over him worked diligently to seal the miscommunication and misapprehension. I wondered why God didn't stop the devil from succeeding in his nefarious schemes in that situation, as he had at the window earlier, and I got my answer as scenes from the rest of his life story unfolded before me.

He never went back to church after that, because of the shame and sense of unworthiness in his mind. It didn't occur to him to try other spiritual families, because he had invested so much in that one and considered it to be the strongest and most "fundamental" ministry in the area. If he wasn't good enough to attend that church, he would be compromising to switch to a weaker one (that kind of thinking was also encouraged by Satan's minions). He did, however, continue to read and study the Bible throughout the years to come, talk about it with whomever he could, and encourage his children to attend worship services, even making sure they had rides every Sunday. He had a few other depressive episodes as time went on, even being committed briefly again some years later, but he was able to work consistently and provide for the needs of the family, which eventually grew to nine children.

It was sad for those children, as they came of age, that their beloved father did not join them in church. (Elizabeth took a long break herself, but then eventually returned to attend with them.) But I was able to see, through the montage of scenes I witnessed, and some explanation from my guides, that God worked all this for good in several ways. One of the biggest was that the children were mercifully kept from the legalistic slavery to man-made rules and self-righteous reputation that plagued so many of their peers in that era and culture. They all became adults who were able to stand on their own without worrying about what people thought of them, and more importantly, they developed humility because of the stigma of what happened to their father and learned to depend on the grace of Christ alone rather than their own goodness or status in men's eyes.

Another blessing that came from all this was that the godly Elizabeth became a more impressive and effective example to her nine children, as she persevered through the myriad of difficulties she faced in life. They all admired her deeply and always remembered her as a woman of prayer who refused to criticize her husband or anyone else who hurt her. Her motto was, "If you can't say anything good, don't say anything at all," and she lived it. She also had a deep trust in God, as exemplified by what she would say anytime there were complaints about a lack of money in the home: "You're not poor, you're a child of the King!"

Elizabeth's faithful prayers for her husband, and the fact that he had a "nervous breakdown" (as they called it) in 1939, also saved him from being killed in World War II like many of his contemporaries. He was turned down by the military when he tried to enlist because of his record of mental instability, though Elizabeth told everyone it was a result of having such a large family.

The government had one big army to feed, she always said. They didn't need another one.

And her prayers over many years were a direct cause of the great joy experienced by a father and son in the last episode we witnessed related to Elizabeth...

Late in his life her husband had a stroke, and the children took turns staying with him for several hours at a time. One of his sons was a pastor, who out of respect had never asked his father about the struggles in his life. But after they had spent a good amount of time together, and knowing his father's time on earth was probably short, the son felt emboldened to do so.

Dad, I always wondered why you stopped going to church, he said. Why haven't you gone all these years?

They told me I did something that couldn't be forgiven. I felt unworthy of going to church.

You mean the "unpardonable sin" that Jesus talks about, when he says there's one sin that won't be forgiven?

I suppose so, the father said. That's it, that's why.

Well, Dad, I've studied those passages where Jesus says that. It's a little difficult to know exactly what he means; different people have different interpretations. But one thing's for sure...the very fact that you think you did means you didn't.

Why's that?

The people who committed an unpardonable sin were completely rejecting Jesus, and saying his miracles were done by the devil. They didn't want to follow Jesus, so they weren't even worried about what he was saying. If you're worried about it, and you want to follow Jesus, you haven't committed that sin. If you did, you wouldn't care about it.

I could see the old man pondering this in his slightly impaired mind, and then I could see two elect angels and a bright manifestation that could only be the hand of the Holy Spirit working in Him. There were no demons anywhere in the vicinity this time.

I want to join your church! The old man suddenly exclaimed, a tear rolling down his cheek.

He started attending every week from then on, and father and son enjoyed sweet fellowship in the Lord all the way up to the father's homegoing about a year later.

Chapter 10

Dark Roads

This was my chance to be the kind of hero I wrote about in my novels, and pretended to be when I was a boy.

Jeff, Steve, and I stood over the young man's bloody body, which had been thrown out of the car during the accident. We were wearing our sheaths, so I was able to crouch down and check for a pulse by pressing my temporary fingers to his neck. I couldn't feel anything, which ironically caused my excitement to increase, because this wouldn't just be a rescue on my part.

It would be a resurrection.

I remembered how Jesus had told me at the beginning of my adventures about a great reward and blessing that awaited me at the end, and wondered if this was it. Ever since I had seen Steve fight off the demons that were afflicting Elizabeth's husband, I had longed for my own opportunity to intervene in a human's life and save the day like he had.

Little did I know then that there were more such opportunities to come, and that I would be completely stunned by the way this one turned out. (Yes, there were actually more surprises than those I told you about in the first few chapters…I wanted you to experience them like I did.)

This particular assignment started long before that fateful night on the road, with me merely watching over that same teenager for what seemed like several weeks. I was alone during all this observation (no Jeff and Steve at that point), and I had not received the temporary body yet, so I was invisible to the young man.

The fact that I was utterly alone with him for those long stretches was something that I noticed and remembered, because of the conspicuous absence of any evil spirits. I never saw even one the whole time, even though the teen was living a life very much like the one described in Ephesians 2:1-3. That passage says, "And you were dead in your trespasses and sins, in which you formerly walked according to the course of this world, according to the prince of the power of the air, of the spirit that is now working in the sons of disobedience. Among them we too all formerly lived in the lusts of our flesh, indulging the desires of the flesh and of the mind, and were by nature children of wrath, even as the rest."

Maybe he had some spiritual life in him, but I didn't see any evidence of it at that time. And it was interesting to note that there didn't have to be any demons anywhere nearby for someone to be filled with all kinds of wickedness. The potential for every sin is already present in our depraved nature, and when demonic temptation does occur it is simply providing more opportunities for that sin to come out. In this

regard, I was reminded also of Jesus words in Mark
7:20-23: "What comes out of a person is what defiles
him. For from within, out of the heart of man, come
evil thoughts, sexual immorality, theft, murder, adul-
tery, coveting, wickedness, deceit, sensuality, envy,
slander, pride, foolishness. All these evil things come
from within, and they defile a person."

While I was watching this teenager, he committed
every sin on that list in one way or another. At his best,
he grudgingly skimmed through his homework and
wasted many hours doodling, talking on the phone,
or playing his rudimentary Atari game system (which
put the time period, I guessed, somewhere in the late
1980s). At his worst, he recorded parts of forbidden
movies from cable TV when his parents weren't around
and hid the VHS tapes in his room, with fake labels to
make them look like family videos in case someone
happened to notice them. The collection of games and
porn were his greatest treasures, while a Divine Book
that should have been was gathering dust on a shelf.

Witnessing this pathetic lifestyle day after day
produced ambivalent feelings in me. On the one hand,
I had sympathy for the young man, since I did similar
things when I was a teen, and in a sense he was a help-
less victim of the world, the flesh, and the devil. And I
grew to care for him after a while, perhaps by virtue of
the sheer amount of time I was with him. But on the
other hand, a righteous disgust and anger also grew
more and more in me as the days slogged on, and I
started gaining an understanding (though relatively
small in comparison) of how God must feel when he
sees all the sins of commission and omission of every-

one in the world all the time. God's holy wrath against evil, which is poured out on his enemies in hell, was becoming far less abstract and enigmatic to me (more on that later).

I think that was one reason why I was required to babysit this particular sinner for such a long time, and when my progress in learning was deemed sufficient, I was pulled away from his presence and placed in a temporary body for the first time since I had my personal audience with the Lord. This time I was on earth, however, which made it doubly disorienting, because instead of a glorious throne room in a perfect heaven, I found myself bouncing in the back seat of a smelly old car on a dark highway.

Jeff and Steve were in the front, and like me they were checking out their sheaths, since this was apparently not a common experience for them either.

I like it, don't get me wrong, Steve was saying, but it always kinda feels like clothes that don't quite fit.

That's because it's not the real one yet, said Jeff, who liked to explain things even if others might know them already. You'll get that at the *Parousia*.

He didn't use that Greek word, of course. Like I told you before, we didn't speak Greek or English or any human language in the IS. But the reverential way that perfected saints referred to the return of Christ was too special to represent with more common words like "coming," or even "resurrection."

Hey, I interrupted from the back, this is a Ford Maverick. And it's even mustard colored, if I'm not mistaken…like my first car!

That God would put us in this rather unique kind

of car made me feel special already, before the main event had even started.

And I *really* felt special when it did.

Jeff and Steve saw the smashed cars up ahead and pulled off the road. It was obvious that we were the first people there, and when I saw the teenager's body sprawled on the pavement, I was sure that this was to be my moment of glory.

After I checked his pulse and found none, I said to myself (not wanting to speak out loud and risk sounding like a rube), *I know what the Lord is up to here…I'll bring him back just in time. I've always heard that angels do things like this. He'd probably go to hell if he died now, but he'll be saved from that, and this traumatic experience will be just what he needs to wake up and see that he needs the Lord. He'll have a great testimony for the rest of his life, and I'll be a part of it!*

I was so excited about what I thought was happening, it took me a while to realize that I didn't know what to do. I hadn't been trained or even instructed in any way, so I looked up at Jeff and Steve from my crouched position.

Should I use the *bara-pneuma* to create new life in him, I asked, (trying not to sound too desperate), or the *asah-pneuma* to re-arrange something, or bring his soul back?

Jeff and Steve looked at each other and shrugged.

I don't know, Jeff said. Are you sure his soul is gone?

I looked back down at the body and scanned it from end to end as if there might be something new to see. I put my fingers to the throat again, still sensing no pulse, and this time my hand came away with blood on it. I stared at the dark red smear, and now it was *really* hitting me that I didn't know what to do. I asked Jesus in my thoughts, but he didn't answer me.

Can't you do something, guys? I said to my companions.

It's your job, not ours, Steve answered. Whatever it is.

But I don't even know what to do, I pleaded, and he's gonna end up in hell.

I didn't know that for sure—God didn't reveal anyone's spiritual state to me definitively, probably so that I would not take any such information back to the land of the living. But it also occurred to me that there were still no evil spirits present at the scene, so maybe that meant the teenager already belonged to Satan and my worst fears were true.

My experienced guides weren't praying for the young man's soul any longer, and I instinctively knew that I shouldn't either. (The practice of praying for the dead is a misguided one that has no warrant in Scripture.) He was gone, so all we could do was check on the passengers of the other car (they were okay) and make an exit in the mustard-colored Maverick when the emergency personnel arrived.

As we drove down the road waiting for an empty stretch where we could disappear without anyone seeing it, I remember thinking about what had happened. (The Lord was still not talking to me, apparently because he wanted me to reflect for a while.)

I was initially surprised that there could be feelings

of failure and disappointment in heaven (or in the IS at least), and that I was sad and even a bit scared about the fate of the teen I had spent so much time with. But then I realized I was still human, and even Christ in his perfect humanity had similar experiences while on this cursed earth. I also was *merely* a man, who despite my great leap of improvement was not even close to omniscient. So why should I be surprised that I could have unmet expectations, and negative emotions as a result?

On the other hand, there was a big difference between my IS response and the one I might have had during my life on earth. Accompanying and offsetting any sorrow and fear was an innate and pervasive confidence of God's providence in the events that were less than desirable to me (and in a way, to him also). Because of this, I immediately found myself thinking about what purposes the Lord may have had for what happened, and this kept me from sliding into sinful responses like frustration or complaining. He wasn't telling me why at this point, and might never, but I made some guesses, and the exercise helped me to end up in praise rather than regret.

I had wondered why God had me observe the young man so intimately and extensively, and besides my growing understanding of his wrath upon sin that I mentioned above, I thought perhaps it was to "put a real face" on the suffering, death, and danger of eternal punishment that I would encounter later on the road. And in a similar vein, he may have placed me in the sheath so that I would feel as well as see the results of the accident and be impacted by it in a greater way. I definitely viewed human sin and death now from a different perspective, which I wouldn't have had without that experience.

I also remember thinking about hell on that ride down the road. God didn't reveal to me for sure where the young man's soul went, but the mere possibility that he was lost forever moved me deeply. I was never made a witness to the torments of hell while I was in heaven, as Jonathan Edwards thought all the perfected saints would be. Maybe that was because I would've then known who some of its residents were, but God could easily have erased any such knowledge from my mind. Rather, I think it was probably unnecessary because like the loving presence of God is perpetually obvious to us in the IS, there is also a settled awareness of the effects his righteous rage must have on anyone from whom it was not propitiated and diverted by Christ's sacrifice on the cross. In a way I can't fully explain to you (what else is new?), the wrath of God is as much of a reality in the next life as his love, though his people do not experience any of the effects of the former. Those who have rejected him feel only the effects of the latter, and of that we were all well aware.

So why aren't the citizens of heaven debilitated, or at least plagued, by the fact that so many souls are suffering in hell, and will be forever? Well, rather than launch into an extensive treatise on the subject, let me just explain it this way for now: During my previous life I would have agreed with C. S. Lewis when he said that hell was the one doctrine of the Bible he would like to do away with if he could, but now I am more in line with the thesis of Thor Ramsey's book *The Most*

Encouraging Book on Hell Ever, that eternal punishment ultimately brings glory to God and that the gospel and love of Christ are rendered pointless without it. I'm sure that Ramsey would have something humorous to say about being mentioned in the same breath as Lewis, since he is a comedian as well as a theologian (and that combination alone makes him worth reading). But I found most of his book to be truly profound, and thoroughly consistent with the wisdom I gained from my experiences.

I especially like the analogy he uses to show that denying the existence or eternality of hell makes Christ's death basically pointless. He says it's like telling a good friend "I love you, man" while walking along a busy city street, and then demonstrating it by randomly running out into the sea of moving cars. It would be a meaningless gesture that couldn't really accomplish anything except getting himself killed in a gruesome fashion. But if he died while pushing his friend out of the path of a careening truck, then that would really mean something, and truly be an expression of sacrificial love.

You can check out Ramsey's book if you want to consider this more, but I'll summarize briefly what I realized in my ruminations about hell that night: When we no longer have the self-aggrandizing and sin-minimizing tendencies of our fallen nature, we will see humanity's rebellion against God for the judgment-worthy crime that it is, and we will understand that hell is merely a continuation and confirmation of the hard-hearted choice that his enemies make to live without him. We will also be deeply moved to praise the Lord constantly and endlessly for his merciful choice to save his people, especially as the light of our heavenly inheritance shines so much more brightly against the backdrop of such horrifying darkness.

As Romans 9:22-24 says, "What if God, desiring to show his wrath and to make known his power, has endured with much patience vessels of wrath prepared for destruction, in order to make known the riches of his glory for vessels of mercy, which he has prepared beforehand for glory—even us whom he has called."

Speaking of darkness, you may have noticed how many of my experiences in the IS involved the terrors of death, in one way or another. You shouldn't be surprised by this, because I warned you early on (in the section about surprises) that as long as the curse of sin still plagues this broken world, it will also haunt the current heaven to a certain degree. Until Satan is thrown into the lake of fire, he still "prowls around like a roaring lion seeking whom he may devour" and can even invade heaven itself with his lies like he did in story of Job.

And if you think the accounts in this book have been dark so far, you haven't seen anything yet. In my next visit to the past, many millions of lives were in danger rather than just one, I encountered "the dragon, that old serpent" himself, and questions arose about the eternal destiny of my own soul.

Chapter 11

Axis of Evil

In my mind I had reconciled the horrors of hell with the justice and righteousness of God, but my own experience in heaven had grown more confusing and distressing to me (which again should not surprise you, because even the sinless Christ experienced those things in his times of testing). Still reeling from my failure with the teenage boy, I had little opportunity to reflect and reach a peace of mind about it, because I soon found myself out of the frying pan and into the fire.

As in some of my previous visits, my next entrance into a new time and place took the form of descending from above (at least in my perspective). I saw from afar a grandiose mountain range punctuated with snow-covered peaks and zoomed in gradually to a secluded hideaway on one of the high inner slopes. Before I even entered the large white chalet, I knew what it was and who was living there, from my previous knowledge and a Divine confirmation of the thoughts in my mind. To those two sources of information I'll add some that I've gathered since then, to give you the best possible picture of what happened during this darkest of all trips into the past.

Another reason I knew who lived in the big mountain house was that I could feel an aura of evil emanating from it. (I sensed this spiritually rather than physically, of course, because I was not wearing a sheath.) It was so strong that I instinctively reached out in my mind to Steve, who was my lone companion on this trip. He was the only one I could talk to at present, because for some reason Jesus was still not communicating with me directly.

As I explained before, the presence of God is experienced and recognized in the IS much more than in our earthly lives, but it still is manifested in different ways at different times. And in this case, for purposes unknown to me, my awareness of it had diminished enough that I was having nagging thoughts about failing again, and in a way far worse than before.

So I said something to Steve along the lines of whether we might be getting in over our heads, but he wasn't able to respond because we were now inside the mountain residence.

It was the Berghof, Adolf Hitler's home and headquarters in the Bavarian Alps, and it was January 24, 1941, at the height of the Nazi dictator's power. A little more than two years into World War II, his armies had conquered all of continental Europe and much of North Africa, and were on the verge of pounding England into submission. Hitler had won every battle he had fought to that point, and the only minor, bittersweet "victory" the Allies could claim was the miraculous survival of the British army by its evacuation from Dunkirk. The Nazi dictator was on top of the world, and not only in the literal sense of where his house was located.

As we passed through the sections of the mansion populated by staff, including a few high-ranking generals waiting in the Great Room, Steve said that he recognized several of the people we saw. I assumed that he meant to say there are Nazis in heaven (the only kind of people considered even worse than serial killers), and if you want proof of that possibility, take a look at the fascinating book by Tim Townsend called *Mission at Nuremberg: An American Army Chaplain and the Trial of the Nazis.* It's about Henry Gerecke, a Lutheran pastor who ministered to Hitler's henchmen after the war was over.

Those renowned trials happened in our "timeline," however, and what I was about to experience raised questions in my mind as to whether there might be other eventualities, or at least one other, where the Nazis win the war and go on to dominate much more of the world.

We found ourselves in Hitler's office on the floor above the Great Room, a waning crescent moon visible through the three floor-to-ceiling windows on the north side of the room, between which hung portraits of the Fuhrer's father and mother. On the west wall was a bigger one of Frederick the Great, and in front of the fireplace under it sat Hitler and his right-hand-man Hermann Goering. They thought they were having a private meeting (which indicated its importance in their minds), but they weren't really alone. They were the only two *human* beings in the room, but they were not the only beings.

Also present was Satan himself, which explained the almost overpowering sense of evil I'd felt as I approached the house, and now was even more intense in the presence of the Lord's greatest Enemy. I would have immediately begged to be rescued from the situation except that there was an equally powerful elect angel there also, and the comfort afforded by his presence lessened my initial panic. The archangel Michael was a veteran of many spiritual battles with the "old dragon," since they were often brought together at crucial moments like this.

As you'll see, the battle between the two fabled spirit beings was primarily one of ideas—a war between their reasoning abilities, and for the minds and hearts of people. The wording of the only scriptural account of their many conflicts reveals this emphasis on rational arguments (and the fact that they converse with one another): "When the archangel Michael, contending with the devil, was disputing about the body of Moses, he did not presume to pronounce a blasphemous judgment, but said, 'The Lord rebuke you'" (Jude 1:9). Also, 2 Corinthians 10:3-5 describes human spiritual warfare in this way: "For though we walk in the flesh, we are not waging war according to the flesh. For the weapons of our warfare are not of the flesh but have divine power to destroy strongholds. We destroy *arguments* and every lofty *opinion* raised against the *knowledge* of God, and take every *thought* captive to obey Christ."

This particular battle between Satan and Michael was also different than one might expect, because neither of them seemed to know what they wanted to accomplish. They were in the Berghof that day because they could tell this was an important meeting at a crucial time in world history (Goering was by far Hitler's most influential advisor). Also, whenever Satan or Michael showed up somewhere, it was almost inevitable that the other would appear also, because the lesser angels under them were no match for either one, and had not been delegated nearly as much authority from God.

Because of my increasing understanding of the spiritual world, it was apparent to me that Hitler and Goering both were regularly influenced by numerous demons, and Satan himself visited them often, which was unusual because the leader of the fallen angels was usually too busy inventing new lies and managing his many minions to afflict a particular person. But Satan enjoyed being with these men, and he enjoyed even more the orgies of death and destruction he was able to orchestrate through them. So at certain key times like this, Lucifer would relieve the other spirits that regularly attended the Nazi leaders and get involved directly.

(Something else that became apparent to me, by the way, was the effect of the mind-altering drugs that both Hitler and Goering took habitually—the Fuhrer was on a cocktail of numerous uppers and downers, and the Reich Marshall was a morphine addict. I don't fully understand all the spiritual mechanics involved, but the use of those chemicals coupled with their hard hearts allowed their minds to be more demonically influenced than they would have been otherwise.)

Even though there were only two men and two

angels involved in the meeting that night, there was so much going on in that room during it that I couldn't possibly remember (nor fully understand) it all. But as always, I will try to communicate the basic gist of what happened.

You wanted to talk to me privately about Russia? Hitler said to Goering, already irritated at the thought. The Nazi ruler had issued a decree a month and a half before (December 8, 1940) to the effect that the entire Wermacht (German military) should begin secret preparations for a war of aggression with the Soviet Union in the spring.

Yes, mein Fuhrer, Goering responded, I wonder if you could explain why you are continuing with the invasion plans, since you have heard Halder and Raeder's objections to it?

I've not heard any objections from them, Hitler said dismissively, to Goering's apparent surprise.

Well, mein Fuhrer, the overweight, round-faced man said. Every time Raeder talks about the British front in the Mediterranean, and the need to take the Suez Canal, he is suggesting that must be finished first.

Never mind Raeder. You're sitting here, not Raeder. Say what you want to say.

I want us to have our glorious prize in the east, Goering said after a pause, and the *lebensraum* that you have always promised us. But I fear that Raeder is right, and this is not the time...yet.

You're afraid that the Third Reich will break on the rocks of Russia like Napoleon did? You don't think me his superior?

I fear only the immeasurable losses that could

occur.

Do you mean the loss of life, the many millions who will die? Are you growing a conscience, Goering?

As I've said before, mein Fuhrer, you are my conscience. I'm merely referring to the loss of resources to our economy, if we are not yet ready for a second front.

That's why we need to do this, my friend, for the oil and food and slave labor that is our right by destiny. And as *I've* said before, that house of Communist Jewery is so rotten, we only have to kick in the door and the whole structure will come crashing down. I seem to remember we had a conversation like this before, at the beginning of the war, about Czechoslovakia. You were worried about the timing then. But we took that country in one day, and then Poland and France in a few months. Who was right about that, hmmm?

The two Nazi leaders sat silently for a few moments, and I was allowed a brief glimpse into their twisted minds and hearts, which I found fascinating. Goering's primary motivation was an utterly selfish form of hedonism—he merely wanted to continue enjoying the spoils of the position of power he had longed for ever since an earlier time in his life when he had been destitute and dependent on the goodwill of others. While making decisions that would affect the lives of tens of millions, his thoughts centered on personal possessions like his elaborate hunting mansion and his collection of stolen art, plus his dream of one day seeing large statues of himself all throughout the German Empire, and small ones in every home. Goering's considerable intelligence and giftedness were used solely for the purpose of self-fulfillment. That's why he said, just before his suicide at Nuremberg, "At least I had twelve good years."

The motivations in Hitler's mind and heart, on the other hand, were much less simple and monochromatic. They were a dark shifting kaleidoscope of factors, from nationalism to "daddy issues" to personal pride, from sexual frustration to false religious ideas to Goering's brand of hedonism. What was common in both men, besides their drug use, was their intense pride and self-righteousness. Yes, the Nazis actually thought they were morally superior to everyone else, which was of course the height of irony. I've often said that pride knows no discrimination, and this proved it. The people with the least reason to be proud often are, and that goes for self-righteousness as well.

Despite the ability that Satan clearly had to influence the men's thoughts and decisions, and the similar power that Michael wielded with the authority of God behind him, neither of the eminent spirits seemed to know exactly what to do in this situation. I surmised from what I already knew that this was because on the one hand, if Germany invaded Russia and won, the Nazis could easily end up ruling the entire world for a long time. If they did not invade Russia, then as allies the two increasingly powerful totalitarian regimes might end up doing so together. Both were desirable outcomes for Satan, and neither were for Michael.

It occurred to me then how important the omniscience of God was to his providential control of the world, and his inevitable victory over evil. He knows the future, while his enemies, thought far more intelligent and powerful than humans, only know the past and the present. Even so, in this situation, Michael apparently was not told by God that Germany would lose the war on the eastern front, and therefore the initiative in the larger conflict. I'll talk later about why this happened, but the Archangel seemed to be operating in "real time," without the benefit of future knowledge.

So I cleared my proverbial throat, and spoke up.

Excuse me, sir, I said. (Or something like that… remember the language we spoke in the IS was very different from earthly ones.)

Be quiet, I'm thinking, Michael said, as firmly and summarily as a sinless creature could without crossing the line into rudeness.

I shut up for a while, as Hitler and Goering continued their discussion and Michael contemplated what to do about it, if anything. Then the Archangel said to me, What?

I told him that if Hitler attacked Russia, it would end up costing him the war, and it would also weaken the USSR enough that they wouldn't be able to take over the world either. So we should want Hitler to invade Russia.

I could never want anyone to do something evil, Michael answered, which such a murderous invasion would be. And I can't make him do it either.

Then he basically quoted James 1:13-15, which says, "Let no one say when he is tempted, 'I am being tempted by God,' for God cannot be tempted with evil, and he himself tempts no one. But each person is tempted when he is lured and enticed by his own desire. Then desire when it has conceived gives birth to sin, and sin when it is fully grown brings forth death."

The Enemy can use his *ra-asah-pneuma* to cause sin, Michael explained further, if and when God allows it. (Apparently Satan has no *bara-pneuma*, or the ability to create, but merely this other delegated form of power and authority.) But we can only use our *asash-pneuma* to cause good or restrain evil.

So could you keep Goering from talking him out of the invasion? I asked, and was then shocked when Satan, who apparently could hear our conversation, spoke directly to me.

Be careful little one, the fallen angel said as I felt something come over me that I couldn't understand or explain. You can know just enough to be dangerous, and you may fail miserably in your attempts to assist the Tyrant.

Did he somehow know that I had been concerned about failure? I asked myself, and then wondered if he could hear my private thoughts as well. I didn't know what to say, so I didn't respond, and he continued.

You think you know the future, but it can be changed. And your interference may cause you to lose favor with your Benefactor. What do you think happened to me in heaven, and to your first parents in the Garden? We were loved by God and had never even disobeyed him like you have—countless times I might add—yet we fell from his favor. What makes you think that won't happen to you, after a few days in heaven, or a few years, or a few thousand years?

He paused for effect, and then added, But don't worry…we fellow refugees from the Tyrant will be here for you when he's had enough of you and casts you out.

The bizarre, inexplicable feeling that I can only

compare to a numb confusion grew stronger inside of my soul. I turned to Steve for help, but he answered with the equivalent of "Don't look at me," and I noticed the same kind of funk was coming over him also.

My soul cried out to Jesus, who I knew was present, but he was still silent. It felt like he was standing by watching, but doing nothing.

It's happening already, Satan said, commanding my attention. I've seen this many times before. He wants to control everything that happens, but his creatures have free will and time is in our hands. It ebbs and flows and deviates from his script, and he can't abide those who have the courage to change it.

Soon I found my perspective paralyzed and only able to focus on Satan, whose appearance was even more impressive than before. I would even use the word beautiful to describe how he was beginning to look to me.

That's enough, Michael said forcefully to Satan and us. Then he addressed me and Steve in particular.

Dear children, he said, the gifts and calling of God are irrevocable. Satan and Adam would not have been able to fall if they were *in Christ* as you are. Your union with the Savior and his representative work on your behalf have made you his brothers, and co-heirs with him.

Now it was his turn to pause for effect.

How long will Christ be loved by the Father? he asked us.

Forever, Steve and I both said, as our strange stupor receded somewhat.

And in him you will be too. How long will Christ

love and serve and obey the Father, and be confirmed in perfect righteousness?

Forever, we said, and were starting to feel almost ourselves again.

So you will be, for you are *in him.*

I directed my gaze at Satan again, but now found him repulsive rather than beautiful.

The Lord has told me that this test for you is complete, Michael said to me. Now you know something of the power of the Enemy, and how susceptible you are if left to yourself. But you've also been shown the surpassing greatness of the Father who chose you, the Son who redeemed you, and the Spirit who sealed you. Resist the devil, and he will flee from you. Even if you find yourself overmatched and tempted, like today, the Lord will always rescue you by some means. Of all those who have come to Him, he has lost none of them—ever. I have never seen it happen, and I've been alive for a very long time.

Meaningless drivel! Satan tried again. From one who only serves the Tyrant because—

His words were suddenly and summarily cut off, and he cowered away from us, closer to the two Nazis conferring by the fireplace.

So now, Michael said to us, what shall we do about this Russia thing?

I don't know, I said, and Steve added the IS equivalent of a shrug. I'm still trying to process everything that just happened.

Yes, you're still learning. The Archangel seemed somewhat amused by us, but then he added much more seriously: I think we should let them do what they want.

So he didn't intervene in any way as Hitler and Goering concluded their conversation, and I got the impression that Satan would also not influence this particular decision, either because he still didn't know what to do or because an unseen hand prevented him. The Fuhrer said he would give the issue further consideration, and the Reich Marshall promised absolute allegiance to whatever decision was made. And then, after Goering left, something else really interesting happened.

It was after 8:00 pm by then, and Hitler told his mistress Eva Braun and the remaining staff that he wanted to watch a film and he should not be disturbed. He settled into an expensive piece of Teutonic furniture in the Great Room, which was by far the most impressive space in the Berghof, with a massive window that could be retracted into the basement below when the weather was warm. A servant adjusted the large Gobelin tapestry on the east wall to uncover the openings from the film projection room, and then completely removed the arras on the opposite side so that wall could serve as a screen.

In the years he lived there prior to the war, Hitler had often sat with Eva and others watching various kinds of movies, many of which were Hollywood productions. He especially enjoyed Mickey Mouse, believe it or not. But after the war started, he made a commitment to abstain from watching films for pleasure, and then would only watch war reels or something else that he thought could aid in his military strategies.

On this particular night, perhaps because Communism was on his mind as he weighed an invasion of the Soviet Union, he told the servant to put on a movie that had recently arrived in the mail. It was the film version of John Steinbeck's *The Grapes of Wrath*, which had just been in the news the previous week for receiving seven Academy Award nominations, including Best Picture, Best Director for John Ford, and Best Actor for Henry Fonda. Hitler knew that he would probably not agree with the philosophy behind much of the movie, and that's why he didn't want Eva or others to watch it with him. But he had no idea just how impactful it would be on his thinking and feelings.

By the end of the next two hours, Hitler was more convinced than ever that immigration in the United States had thoroughly mongrelized the general populace and was appalled by how degenerate the common people of America had become. If even farmers of Anglo-Saxon stock could succumb to such racial and moral disintegration, he concluded, the American military would be a pushover for the Wehrmacht. Further, he found himself growing angry and a bit fearful at the apparent creeping Communism in our burgeoning country, as evidenced by the popularity of this book and other works by the famous author, who Hitler thought to be a Jew because *Stein* was a part of his name.

The truth is, John Steinbeck was neither a Communist nor a Jew, and actually had written a letter in 1940 about his ancestry in which he said, "On both sides and for many generations we are blond and blue-eyed to a degree to arouse the admiration and perhaps envy of the dark-complexioned Hitler." And

Steinbeck's middle name was Ernst. But Hitler didn't know any of that, and the die was cast that night in the Fuhrer's mind, especially because the film was so emotionally affecting. The crazed fascist determined once and for all that he would conquer Russia so that his most hated ideology could not be spread any further. And before the year was out he would also unilaterally—and seemingly inexplicably—declare war on the United States (which would prove to be another major blunder).

It was ironic that Steinbeck would play such a role in Hitler's failures, because the American writer had actually volunteered as a propaganda writer for the Allies during the war (as George Orwell did in England). Also, *The Grapes of Wrath* ends with the main character seemingly transformed into a mythical spirit destined to play a key role in righting the wrongs of the world. And here at the height of Nazi power (literally and figuratively), Steinbeck and the ghost of Tom Joad won the greatest victory in their war on injustice.

This all happened by Divine providence, of course, which highlights another irony. Many of Steinbeck's beliefs and ideas had actually been inspired by the Enemy and were contrary to the truth of Scripture, but they were ultimately used for the good purpose of delivering God's people (and the rest of the world around them) from a dark future. This happens constantly, not only in the secular arts, but also in the scientific and military endeavors of people who do not believe in Christ (equally evidenced in WWII). As Ecclesiastes 2:25 says, "To the sinner he has given the business of gathering and collecting, only to give to one who pleases God."

After the movie was over and Hitler's fateful decision had been made, Michael sent the spiritual equivalent of a smile emoji our way, and Steve and I were airlifted out of the Berghof and back into the heavenly realms, where our reason was fully restored. Even better, Jesus spoke directly with me for the first time in a while. Knowing my questions before I asked them, he explained that our souls were no longer able to sin in the IS (and in the future new heavens and earth), but that didn't mean life would be boring there (as I obviously had found out). Sinning and failing at a difficult task were two different things, and emotions like disappointment, anger, and some kinds of fear were a part of how we were created as humans and not necessarily immoral. He told me that we could still experience suspense and doubts about the outcome of the adventures he had planned for us, because we would never know everything like he did, and we would never know ahead of time whether things would go the way we thought they should.

For example, he said, I can tell you that at the time you just left, Hitler actually *does* have the ability to conquer Russia when he attacks it in the spring. The invasion will come as a surprise to Stalin, who in his own arrogance refuses to believe that Hitler has lied to him (even though he did to everyone else). The German armies will roll easily across 2000 miles of the Soviet border in the initial offensive and occupy over 500,000 square miles of Soviet territory in less than six months. The Russian military will simply not be developed and disciplined enough by that time to stop them from taking Moscow and the other major cities. If everything stays at it was during your visit, the Nazis *will* conquer the world.

What—? I started to say, flabbergasted and beginning to have doubts again about the fixedness of history. But then I also was starting to understand that we as humans would never completely know the sovereign plan of God, even in heaven, and would always be living out the adventure of finding it out as we went and participating in it by God's gracious design for an abundant life of adventure.

So…, I said, the invasion will have to be delayed, right?

Good thinking, the Lord said. Can you figure out a way to do it?

Me? I said incredulously.

Yes, you. We'll let you see everything that happens in the following months, and you'll come up with a plan and use the *asah-pneuma* to make it work. If you can.

Not knowing what else to do at the moment, I looked at Steve.

You didn't do very well the last time, he offered.

Thanks a lot, I told him, but what he said seemed to make me want to do this even more. So I told the Lord that I would.

After thoroughly studying events that took place at various places and times during the following months (I *really* can't describe how that all happened), I ended up in another office of Hitler's a couple months later, on March 27. It was the great study at the Reich Chancellery in Berlin, and this time a portrait of Bismarck was looking down on a gathering of the Fuhrer and all his top military officers. The man with the Hitler moustache was so agitated on this occasion that he couldn't even sit down, having just heard about a *coup* in Yugoslavia by a gang of Serbians who were unwilling to continue as a puppet state of the Third Reich.

Satan himself showed up again here, probably because he knew that significant decisions might be made that could affect the amount of moral chaos he was able to inflict on the world. I was alone this time, with no Michael or Steve, and the old dragon immediately became overconfident as a result.

You again? he said to me. They're really scraping the bottom of the barrel up there. (That was the gist, anyway.)

As the meeting began and progressed, it seemed apparent to me that Satan had decided to throw in with the Nazi regime rather than the Communists, and therefore wanted the Germans to win the upcoming war in Russia. I wasn't sure why, but maybe he figured that Marxism wasn't sustainable for the long term, or that the Soviet Union would eventually lose a cold war with America. (Satan isn't omniscient, but he *is* very smart.)

I won't be able to explain how I was becoming so adept at my newfound IS abilities of selective mind-reading and spiritual manipulation, but I can tell you the highlights of what I did during the meeting.

Hitler was so angry at the Yugoslavs for defying him (and insulting his pride) that he was ready to declare war on them right then and there. He paced around vigorously, shouting at the top of his lungs in one of the wildest rages of his entire life—a lot like Bruno Ganz in that movie *Downfall*. Because of his own preternatural knowledge, Satan began to use his *ra-asah-pneuma* to settle Hitler down and make him more rational, because an invasion of Yugoslavia would delay the one planned for Russia and extend the latter into the deadly winter that had stopped Napoleon and the Swedes in the past. So with some of God's *asah-pneuma*, I countered Satan's influence and allowed Hitler's temper tantrum to continue. I also prevented no less than three of his henchmen (including Goering) from raising objections during the meeting, by removing some nationalistic restraints on their fear of losing their jobs (or lives) if they argued with the brutal dictator.

In short, I took a page from Michael's book and let them all do what they wanted to do.

Before the meeting was over, Hitler had commanded his generals to attack Yugoslavia, which actually became his biggest blunder (tied with declaring war on the U.S.), because the unnecessary military operation in that small Balkan country caused the Russian invasion to be postponed for four weeks. Several months later, an unusually early winter arrived just before the Germans could take Moscow, Leningrad, or Stalingrad, and the rest, as they say, is history.

I received a "Well done" from Jesus that was beyond thrilling, and I was now more than ready for a final adventure, which would contain a hint of the possible connection between all of the things I'd experienced.

Chapter 12

Beatific Visions

It's a testimony to how exciting my IS adventures were that I hadn't really thought much about my own death. But during a brief downtime for my soul (perhaps so that it could rest from my battles with evil), I did start to wonder what was happening with my loved ones back on earth as a result of my passing.

I imagined my wife realizing in the morning that I wasn't going to wake up, feeling my cold body, and trying to figure out how to tell the children that I was dead. I thought about the doctors saying it was a heart attack or stroke, and how I shouldn't have eaten so much fat or drank so much sweet tea. I pictured my family planning a memorial service, which would be somewhat complicated because they would have to figure out who to invite. (My family and some friends still love me and think well of me, but others view me as some kind of monster who could never be trusted again.)

I wondered what people said about me when they heard about my death—I could guess what was said in public but would've liked to be a fly on the wall for the private conversations. (Maybe God knew that would've been too much for me to handle, and that's why he didn't let me witness any of it.) But because I was trusting in sovereign providence like never before, and enjoying the IS so much, I found myself feeling thankful that my family could cash in on my life insurance and wouldn't have to worry about overdue bills anymore. And then I also found myself hoping my wife would remarry, because she definitely deserved someone better than me.

Thinking about what else might have happened on earth since I died led me to make some calculations about how long I'd been in the IS. It seemed like a few weeks at least, and more like a month, because of the extended times spent watching the teenager and researching Hitler's decisions.

Has it been long enough at this point for me to ask the Lord to bring someone else into Lynn's life, I wondered, *or would this be too soon for her?*

I didn't get to ponder that or any other issues further, because I was soon transported (alone again) to a big city that I didn't recognize, and to a meeting that was very different from the ones with the Nazis, but almost as depressing.

Eight people sat around a table in a board room, four men and four women, but one of the women was clearly the visionary of the group and therefore the center of attention. She was a tall and strong but feminine figure in her mid-sixties, and one of my first thoughts when I saw her was that she reminded me of my wife. I immediately wondered if maybe this *was* Lynn, and I was now visiting the future for the first time, but then I realized it might be just because I'd been thinking about her. Perhaps because of the limitations of my "eyeless" IS perception, or for whatever reason, I couldn't tell whether it was Lynn or not at this point.

As if in response to my curiosity about the older woman, I was given a glimpse into her currently distressed heart. She had long dreamed of starting a home for needy single mothers that, unlike other similar missions, would allow them to keep their children with them rather than being separated from them. Lynn had that same dream ever since she was a teenager, so maybe this *was* a future version of my wife. But all I knew for sure at this point was that the woman's heart was very heavy: this non-profit board of directors existed to facilitate her dream, but right now it looked like it would never become a reality.

Mrs. Huck, one of the men said to her, this board was formed almost two years ago, and we're no more solvent than we were at the beginning. In fact, it's worse now after the purchase of the farmhouse. I suggested moving that family in from the project temporarily, but I never expected them to bring so many relatives in. I think the total is fourteen right now in the house, if I'm not mistaken…it would be hard to relocate that many people, let alone replace their rent with the meager donations we've been receiving.

I tried to think of whether I knew of anyone named Huck that Lynn might have remarried after I died, but couldn't, and now I heard the woman speak for the first time.

Mr. Lees, she said, you have a banker's mind, and a very good one I might add. But God's math is different from ours.

I'm afraid platitudes won't suffice anymore, he

retorted.

It took my first husband and I over a year to start the Anchorage House for men's rehabilitation in Albany, Mrs. Huck said, and five for the Women's Division. You weren't on the board of the Women's Mission here in Atlanta like some of us were, but we can all testify to the perseverance needed for that work to begin.

So this can't be Lynn, I thought, *because I was her first husband and we never lived in Georgia, let alone started a recovery ministry there.*

I'm not the only one ready to quit, the banker said, and Mrs. Huck looked around to see some heads lower slightly. Even those who were with you at the Mission think that this is different. In fact, I'm so sure that this project should be abandoned that I have chosen not to renew my $25,000 note. It will be rescinded as of the end of the business day tomorrow. I'm very sorry, but this is the way it has to be.

I saw the old woman's shoulders droop and was given a brief glimpse inside of her soul, just long enough to confirm that she wasn't my wife, though there were definitely some similarities. What I saw also produced in me a great admiration for her—she had been twice widowed and profoundly tested by many more trials, including the loss of a daughter to cancer, her own bout with that terrible disease, and the painful divorces several of her children had gone through. Yet she had persevered in serving the Lord and had accomplished much for him—the Women's Mission she started in Atlanta had been the first of its kind in the U.S. Now she longed to pioneer another new kind of ministry, but she knew that without the banker's note it was doomed to failure before it started.

I was even more impressed when I saw her heart choose to trust God about all this, as she responded with kindness to the banker and the other opposing board members. She then closed the meeting with a beautiful prayer of faith.

If God wants Village Atlanta to happen, she said as she rose to leave, he'll just have to do a miracle by the end of the day tomorrow.

It was then I knew what my own mission on this trip was to be. I scoped the minds and hearts of the board members as they left the meeting, well enough to know that I wouldn't be able to change their perspectives anytime soon—least of all the banker's. So I had to get the money from somewhere else. Psalm 50:10 came to my mind, that "God owns the cattle on a thousand hills," and some other ideas as well, so I just stepped out in faith and acted on them, rather than waiting for better ones to arise.

I navigated my soul to the morning of the next day and to a bank in the nearby city. When I arrived at the bank, however, I needed a sheath for what I was being led to do, and I had to get it while on the ground, so I wouldn't fall from the sky and create a scene among the passersby. So I shifted into a nearby phone booth, and as I did I realized that this was definitely *not* the future (no phone booths since 2010 or so). I stepped out of the phone booth dressed in a new body and a gray double-breasted pinstripe suit with a black shirt, like the outfit worn by Tubbs in Miami Vice. I laughed out loud because I now knew what it felt like to be

Superman, and that I was in the 1980s.

I felt somewhat uncomfortable again in the sheath, but perhaps more so because of the fashion, which I never would have worn during my life on earth. But the excitement of what I was doing more than made up for that.

Once inside the bank, I found a new accounts manager and sat in a chair across from her desk, trying to decide whether to unbutton the bulky jacket or leave it be. Not sure exactly what would happen here, but following a spiritual version of instinct, I told the lady that I wanted to open up a new account. When we got to the part where she asked me for a driver's license or some other form of ID, I patted the back pocket of my pants and discovered that there was a fully equipped wallet there. (Without getting into the issue of exactly when and how God created the world, I will say that this proved beyond a doubt that he can indeed create something out of nothing.)

You already have an account with us, she said after a few moments (more proof of creation *ex nihilo*).

I do? I said. Oh, yes, I do.

Do you want to open another account?

No.... How much is in that one?

Forty thousand dollars.

Oh, hmmm. Well, I guess I want to withdrawal that, and close the account. That's what I meant...close the account, not open one. Sorry.

She looked perplexed, but started to shift her papers around anyway. Then I mystified her more when the Spirit gave me some further ideas.

Wait, I said. How about we leave it open, and....

Can I have all the deposits that come into it be automatically paid out to a charity? I'm gonna make a loan to someone and when they pay, I want increments to be sent back to the charity anonymously. That way they'll have to exercise faith by paying it back, but they'll always have what they need.

I smiled from ear to ear, which felt weird because the face of my sheath was still being broken in. The bank officer, however, seemed more confused than amused.

Yes, we can do that, she said. What's the name of the party that will be making payments?

Village Atlanta, I answered.

And what's the name of the charity you would like to pay?

Village Atlanta.

She was clearly having trouble following my logic, but she arranged everything as I said without any complaints, and I left the bank with an unnamed cashier's check for $40,000.

A mailed envelope wouldn't reach Mrs. Huck before the end of the day, so I had to take a cab to her office on the campus of the North Avenue Presbyterian Church. It was warm in the cab, so I took off the sportcoat, and when I arrived at the church I was so excited to get out that I left it in the backseat after paying the driver with cash from my *ex nihilo* wallet. (I wondered later whether the coat just disappeared from the cab at some point, or if the driver added it to his wardrobe, or what.)

No surprise that Mrs. Huck was praying when I found her in the office. I was so excited to be doing this, because it had been a fantasy of mine ever since the Spurgeon/Dickens encounter. So I immediately blurted out that this was an anonymous gift of a no-interest loan for $40,000, which should be just enough to cover the banker's note and the unpaid interest expense, and gave her the account number from the bank where payments on the loan could be made. All the while my new face was being broken in further by my incessant smiling.

Are you sure you want this to be anonymous? Mrs. Huck said, all smiles herself now.

Yes, of course it's anonymous, I said. You don't know me.

Okay, she said, her grin somewhat amused and questioning now. I don't know you, if you say so. But thank you so much…you don't know how much this means to our ministry, and what a faith-builder it is.

Oh, I do. But this is a great experience for me too. I'm learning to live by faith more myself, even in the next life.

She smiled in the same way again, and then said an inspiring prayer of praise and thanksgiving. I think she may have used a name a few times in the prayer when referring to me, so it occurred to me for the first time that my sheath might have looked like someone she knew.

Is there anything I can do for *you*? she asked when she was done praying.

No, I don't think so, I said. Well, except…. Is there a phone booth around here?

When I was back in heaven, I got another thrilling "Well done" from Jesus, whose slightly amused smile was something like Mrs. Huck's (or vice versa). Then the Lord sent me back to Atlanta several years later, in the summer of 1989, to see what had happened at Village Atlanta as a result of my work. This time my soul was "unsheathed" so I could be more aware of the spiritual blessings that had accrued.

The big farmhouse had been transformed into a cozy home for five single mothers and their children, and work had begun on a larger facility behind it. The rooms in the house were all decorated differently to provide a unique space for each woman—one had a beach theme, for example, and another various shades of lavender. I could tell there was genuine happiness and more than a little spiritual life and growth in the house, but my observation was cut short when I noticed that Mrs. Huck was meeting two other people outside to give them a tour. I wanted to see if she was happy herself, and what she would say as she showed them around, so I "zoomed in" to watch them more closely.

I was about to be even more shocked than when I met the two famous Charleses in Victorian London, or Hitler in the Bavarian Alps.

Hi Aunt Elsie, said a vaguely familiar woman of about forty years of age, as she joyfully hugged Mrs. Huck. It's great to see you.

I'm so glad you could come, the older lady replied, all the way from Pennsylvania! And then Mrs. Huck looked at the teenage girl who had come with the woman, and added, Oh, my how you've grown!

Hi Aunt Elsie, the girl said as they hugged one another.

I fixed my eyeless stare on the teen, then did the IS

equivalent of a double take. It really *was* my wife Lynn, more than 25 years younger than the last time I had been with her. Her big head of bold, curly blond hair also removed all doubt that we were in the 80s.

I followed the three women on their tour of the house, trying to figure out what this all meant, especially in relation to my other adventures, and admiring the sincerity and strength in Lynn's heart, which would only grow in her through the coming years. (There were many similarities between Lynn and her Great Aunt, by the way, in the shared height and strength of their physical frames, but even more so in the visionary and compassionate powers of their souls.)

At one point during the tour of the house, God allowed me to hear what Lynn was thinking, loud and clear...

This is what I want to do with my life, she thought, and decided shortly after that to take a college major in Family Consumer Science (a more challenging version of Home Economics), so she could prepare to do the kinds of things Aunt Elsie had done. The idea of ministering to single moms together with their children was especially impactful on her young mind, and stayed with her for the rest of her life.

This was the first time I saw someone I knew personally in the IS, and I would have loved to re-discover what my dear wife was like at 18 years old. (Even though I had been dating her at that time, I don't remember much from that far back.) But I didn't get a chance, because immediately after I heard those fateful thoughts about her life's dream, I was reunited with her at age 45.

Chapter 13

Next Life

Have you ever had a dream where you couldn't breathe, and at the last second, before you are about to suffocate, you wake up? Then you gulp in the air as you come back to consciousness, relieved that it was just a dream? That's what it felt like for me when I found myself back in the same bed where I'd left my body—except for the dream part. As I told you before, I definitely did *not* dream the things that happened to me in the IS.

My chest heaved, my mouth gasped, and my eyes opened to see the dark shape of Lynn lying beside me. Her back was to me, and she was fast asleep. My first instinct was to wake her up, but then I remembered how hard she worked during the day and how much she desperately needed her sleep at night. I had long ago made it a policy not to disturb her unless it was absolutely necessary.

So I turned quietly onto my back and took stock of my surroundings. The clock to my left said 3:06 am, and the usual white noise was playing on the radio (another sleep aid for Lynn). Even though I'd been in the IS for weeks, somehow I knew that I'd returned on the same night I left, with very little time elapsed (if any—I'm not sure what time it was when my journey began).

I'm glad I had that policy of not waking Lynn up, because the more I thought about what happened to me, the more I was afraid to tell her or anyone else about it. I had experienced such agony and depression for the last several months that my family and friends were already seriously worried about my mental state. If I told them that I had gone to heaven and traveled back in time, they would never believe me. They'd think I was experiencing a "break with reality" as a result of my trauma or trying to cope with it by creating some kind of psychological distraction. Worst case scenario, people might conclude that whatever form of madness or demonic delusion had led me to go astray in the first place was still running its full course, and all my repentant apologies and life changes had been essentially meaningless.

So I made two determinations as I lay in my bed that night: One was that I would not tell anyone what happened to me unless or until I was sure the time was right, and the second was that I would do my best to figure it all out. I'd play detective to find out whether my IS adventures actually fit with reality, and if there was some kind of over-arching purpose for them.

I spent a lot of my free time in the next few months researching and reflecting on my experiences, and when I talked to people about things that happened in the past, or they asked me why I was reading a certain book, I would say that I was working on a novel about dying, going to heaven, and traveling back in time. Whenever I talked about it, I always presented it as a fictional account.

I started my investigation with the Aunt Elsie episode, because that was where my adventures ended and it was easy to prove or disprove at least parts of the story. And it turned out that all of it was totally consistent with eyewitness accounts I heard. Lynn confirmed that she did indeed take a trip to Atlanta in the summer of 1989 (which I vaguely remember myself), and that "*This is what I want to do with my life*" were the exact words in her mind when she was touring the house for single mothers. But there was more: I found out that Lynn actually owns a copy of a self-published book called *A Life of Faith: My Journey*, by Elsie Moses Huck Detweiler, as told to Douglas V. Jewson, M.D.

As I pored through the biography, I was amazed to find the details fit precisely with what I had experienced on my last IS trip, right down to the story (on page 218) of a ministry-saving anonymous gift of a $40,000 loan. I was interested to learn that the banker who had opposed Elsie and withdrawn his $25,000 note ended up leaving the board shortly after that, and that the way she tells the story makes it sound like she knew the new lender, which confirmed my suspicions that my sheath had resembled somebody she recognized.

The fact that this final encounter included Lynn led me to wonder if others were related to her as well, and I realized that parts of them seemed familiar to things I had heard about her and her family. The first domino to fall was the story of Elizabeth—it soon became very clear that this was Lynn's grandmother, from whom she got her middle name. While talking with her dad and his siblings about their mother, I heard numerous facts that fit with everything I had learned in the IS about the remarkable woman who had raised nine children successfully, despite her husband's bouts with mental illness. I also heard directly from their son, who is still a pastor (now 83 years old), about that dear man's end-of-life conversion, and it happened just as I related it in Chapter 9.

After that, it didn't take long before I realized that Lynn's great grandmother's name was Mae, and the events of my story about her were confirmed by a perusal of various documents that had been compiled for a family reunion, as well as discussions with some of her grandchildren. One of the most interesting things I found in my research was a reproduction of the entire newspaper story about the death of Mae's husband, which described the cause of death as "acute indigestion" despite the fact that his son and others insisted that he'd been electrocuted.

The final piece of fascinating information I got from Lynn (with some subtle leading questions) was that when she was a teenager and had just broken up with her boyfriend, another young man from her past had started calling her and asking her to reconnect with him. She might have done that (against her better judgment) because the boy was very good-looking, but it never happened because he was killed in a car accident before they could get together.

In those four adventures, God clearly seemed to be showing me events in the past that somehow contributed to Lynn's salvation, and to her developing into the great woman of God she had become. (He'd even allowed me to *participate* in one of them: She would've never have been inspired by Aunt Elsie's ministry if that interest-free loan hadn't come through in the nick of time!) I now felt sure that those four visits to the past—Mae, Elizabeth, Elsie, and the ill-fated teenage boy—were all ways of allowing me to see the complex tapestry that Divine providence had woven in Lynn's life.

But what about the trips to ancient Israel, and Victorian London, and WWII Germany? The purposes of those were harder to guess, but first let me tell you what I discovered as I searched the historical records to find out whether the things I wrote about in those chapters could have really happened.

I already mentioned that the scriptural accounts about Abraham and Jacob fit perfectly with those stories, down to the actual wording of the dialogue. But I had to dig deeper into the biographies of Charles Spurgeon and Charles Dickens to see if that clandestine meeting was possible, and what I found was absolutely uncanny. For example, Spurgeon's autobiography contains a story of two large donations—signed "A. B." with a note accompanying the second—that allowed the building of his orphanage to continue, and those gifts were given during Dickens' later years. When I saw the content of the final letter Dickens wrote two days before he died, and the last page of fiction he wrote just before his fatal stroke, I couldn't believe how well they fit with the conversation between the two men.

And speaking of uncanny, William L. Shirer's classic book *The Rise and Fall of the Third Reich* and

Anthony Read's *The Devil's Disciples: Hitler's Inner
Circle* both contain extensive details about Hitler's
decision to invade Russia that support and never contradict what I wrote in Chapter 11—including the
meeting with Goehring on January 24 of 1941 that
ended at 8:00 pm, just in time for Hitler to watch a
movie. I checked old Academy Awards records to see
when *The Grapes of Wrath* was in the news for its Oscar
nominations (it was exactly at that time), and I found
some quotes by little-known historians about how the
movie had affected Hitler (in a web article by Stephen
J. Whitfield that references Gerhard L. Weinberg's
book *World in the Balance: Behind the Scenes of World
War II*). There are even records online that corroborate
the size of the moon outside the windows on that particular night.

   I was utterly convinced by then, just a few months
after that fateful night, that there was no way I could
have dreamed all of this, and there was no way my
mind could have made it all up. But what still remained
a mystery was the *purpose* for these trips to foreign
places in the distant past, at crucial moments in history.
Because I didn't have any other lead, I found myself
going back to what I already understood about the
later events in America, and how they all were related
to Lynn in some way. And I began to see the earlier
ones through that lens as well.

   The events in the lives of the Patriarchs (Abraham
and Jacob) *were* related to Lynn's salvation, sanctifica-
tion, and service for the Lord, because the covenant
grace given to those fathers back then was the foundation of the mercies she had received. Abraham was

her father in the faith and Jacob was her namesake, since she is a member of God's chosen people (Gal. 3:7-9, 6:15-16). The trials and testings those men went through, as well as the completely undeserved rewards they were given, were types of what all believers would experience in the New Covenant age.

I assumed it would be much harder to make a connection between my angelic wife and the demonic Adolf Hitler. But once I started thinking in terms of God's providence in history, it soon dawned on me that if the Nazi leader had either conquered or maintained peace with Russia, the United States may have eventually fallen to one or both of those totalitarian regimes, and the Christian schools that were so influential in Lynn's young life might have never existed.

Maybe that's why God chose for my IS trips to include such far-flung adventures—so I would not fail to see (and tell others) that the tapestry of our lives includes a multitude of threads from times and places that seem very remote and unconnected to our own experience on earth. And that our own choices can have rippling effects far beyond what we could ever imagine.

That said, I'm still not sure why the Lord let me witness the interaction between Charles Spurgeon and Charles Dickens. Maybe that conversation somehow led to the salvation of a child in Spurgeon's orphanage or a reader of *Edwin Drood*, who then became one of Lynn's ancestors, or led one of them to the Lord, or something like that. Or maybe the Lord, knowing that I love history and those two men in particular, just wanted to show me how totally cool heaven will be.

So I believe that the answer to the mystery, and the common theme of my IS experiences, was Lynn. God wanted me to see some of the many threads that went into the supernatural work of art that is my beloved wife. This might not seem as dramatic or provocative as you anticipated, but the truth is not always so. I can only speculate on the reasons why—perhaps God couldn't show me my own past for some reason, and Lynn was the person I know the best; or it would help me to further correct the wrongs I'd done, and even make up for them in some way (which I've longed to do); or the Lord simply delights in the marriage relationship more than any other, because it's a picture of Christ's love for the church (Eph. 5:22-33).

Maybe it's all of the above, and/or something else I haven't thought of, "For my thoughts are not your thoughts, neither are your ways my ways, declares the Lord. For as the heavens are higher than the earth, so are my ways higher than your ways and my thoughts than your thoughts" (Isa. 55:8-9).

One thing I do know, however, is that I myself will never be the same again. What I've recounted here may have all been *about* Lynn, but it was *for* me (and for you, if you'll learn something from it). In addition to all the new perspectives that I mentioned in the early chapters of this book, my new awareness of Divine providence in my wife's "pre-history" has caused me to be so much more grateful and thankful, which is a corrective to the foundational sin problem that led to all my others. It reminds me of the climactic scene in Alan Moore's graphic novel *Watchmen*, when the formerly cynical and detached superman Dr. Manhattan realizes for the first time what a "thermodynamic miracle" life is, especially since it emerges from the midst of evil and suffering (and sometimes because of it). Or if you prefer a more family friendly analogy, the effect all this had on me was a lot like the last thirty minutes of *It's A Wonderful Life*.

And it's all a part of the larger process of God restoring and renewing me as his son and servant. As a result of my sins, I'd suffered excruciating emotional pain and other extreme consequences, including the loss of my career, my reputation, and $75,000 I didn't have (and counting). But I'd also truly repented and began walking with God and my wife again with a clean conscience, therefore regaining the things that matter the most. Writing this book helped me to focus more on what I have and less on what I've lost.

I never did tell Lynn (or anyone else) that these things happened to me, knowing that I could be thought of as "a few fries short of a Happy Meal" and committed to the hospital. But the value of these remarkable stories and the idea of publishing them as fiction finally motivated me to write them down. Lynn is probably the only one who would actually be able to get me committed, so I'm anxious to find out what she thinks of this book. But then again, she's always been too busy with more important things to read any of the others I've written, so I might be safe after all.

Assuming that I *don't* get locked up for what I've written here, I think I know what the "great reward" is that Jesus said I would receive after I completed the missions he gave me in the IS. From now on I would have *a new life here*, in addition to a glorious future in heaven. As it is for all the saints, the former becomes a foretaste of the latter—and in my case, vice versa! So now I pray these words with an understanding I never had before: "Thy kingdom come, Thy will be done, on earth as it is in heaven."

Visit

CruciformPress.com

for more Cruciform Fiction books
as well as

*Bible Studies for Women
by Keri Folmar*

and more than sixty Christian titles
from top authors such as

*John Piper
Tim Challies
Jerry Bridges*

and many more